Introduction

Pupils' written work

Abacus textbooks are unique in that they pr
how their work should be recorded. Pupils sl
guidance, which will make marking their wc
focused.

Marking pupils' work

Clearly it is important that pupils' work is seen and checked by the teacher regularly, but it is not necessary for all work to be marked by the teacher. Decisions about which work should be teacher-marked, and how it should be marked will be made alongside the need to maximise time available for teaching and guiding pupils through their activities.

A suggested approach within Abacus is to make these decisions Unit by Unit. Decide, for example, for each Unit, which parts you want to mark, and which parts the pupils can mark.

Marking the 'Explores'

The 'Explores' should generally be marked by the teacher. The 'Explores' often require a systematic approach, and the answers give suggestions for these. These approaches can be communicated to the pupils, to help them develop systematic ways of working. Also, the pupils' responses to the 'Explores' may well vary because of the often open-ended nature of the activities.

For many 'Explores' you may want to ask the pupils to work in pairs or groups, possibly leading to a group display of the results of their 'exploration'.

Contents

Number Textbook 1

Rounding

1a. 4760 fans	**b.** 4800 fans	**c.** 5000 fans
2a. 3950 fans	**b.** 4000 fans	**c.** 4000 fans
3a. 8270 fans	**b.** 8300 fans	**c.** 8000 fans
4a. 2320 fans	**b.** 2300 fans	**c.** 2000 fans
5a. 6060 fans	**b.** 6100 fans	**c.** 6000 fans
6a. 4600 fans	**b.** 4600 fans	**c.** 5000 fans
7a. 6480 fans	**b.** 6500 fans	**c.** 6000 fans
8a. 3990 fans	**b.** 4000 fans	**c.** 4000 fans
9a. 9150 fans	**b.** 9100 fans	**c.** 9000 fans
10a. 7330 fans	**b.** 7300 fans	**c.** 7000 fans

❷ **1.** $10\,000 - 4762 = 5238$ fans   **2.** $10\,000 - 3954 = 6046$ fans
3. $10\,000 - 8267 = 1733$ fans   **4.** $10\,000 - 2318 = 7682$ fans
5. $10\,000 - 6059 = 3941$ fans   **6.** $10\,000 - 4596 = 5404$ fans
7. $10\,000 - 6479 = 3521$ fans   **8.** $10\,000 - 3987 = 6013$ fans
9. $10\,000 - 9146 = 854$ fans   **10.** $10\,000 - 7328 = 2672$ fans

11. $4762 + 8267 = 13\,029 \rightarrow 13\,000$ people
12. $4596 + 9146 = 13\,742 \rightarrow 14\,000$ people
13. $3987 + 7328 = 11\,315 \rightarrow 11\,000$ people
14. $6059 + 2318 = 8377 \rightarrow 8000$ people
15. $3954 + 3987 = 7941 \rightarrow 8000$ people
16. $6479 + 8267 = 14\,746 \rightarrow 15\,000$ people
17. $4762 + 4596 = 9358 \rightarrow 9000$ people
18. $8267 + 7328 = 15\,595 \rightarrow 16\,000$ people

❷ **11.** $13\,029 \rightarrow 13\,000$ **12.** $13\,742 \rightarrow 13\,500$
13. $11\,315 \rightarrow 11\,500$ **14.** $8377 \rightarrow 8500$
15. $7941 \rightarrow 8000$ **16.** $14\,746 \rightarrow 14\,500$
17. $9358 \rightarrow 9500$ **18.** $15\,595 \rightarrow 15\,500$

Rounding

1. $2 \cdot 7 \rightarrow 3$ **2.** $5 \cdot 9 \rightarrow 6$ **3.** $6 \cdot 4 \rightarrow 6$ **4.** $2 \cdot 2 \rightarrow 2$ **5.** $3 \cdot 1 \rightarrow 3$
6. $7 \cdot 7 \rightarrow 8$ **7.** $8 \cdot 1 \rightarrow 8$ **8.** $5 \cdot 3 \rightarrow 5$ **9.** $4 \cdot 5 \rightarrow 5$ **10.** $3 \cdot 6 \rightarrow 4$
11. $2 \cdot 4 \rightarrow 2$

Number Textbook 1

Place-value **N1**

12. 65·2 m → 65 m   **13.** 37·6 m → 38 m   **14.** 44·1 m → 44 m
15. 51·9 m → 52 m   **16.** 32·4 m → 32 m   **17.** 98·9 m → 99 m
18. 82·7 m → 83 m   **19.** 101·3 m → 101 m   **20.** 99·9 m → 100 m
21. 67·09 m → 67 m   **22.** 63·13 m → 63 m   **23.** 59·49 m → 59 m

@ **12.** 65·2 m → 70 m   **13.** 37·6 m → 40 m   **14.** 44·1 m → 40 m
   15. 51·9 m → 50 m   **16.** 32·4 m → 30 m   **17.** 98·9 m → 100 m
   18. 82·7 m → 80 m   **19.** 101·3 m → 100 m   **20.** 99·9 m → 100 m
   21. 67·09 m → 70 m   **22.** 63·13 m → 60 m   **23.** 59·49 m → 60 m

---

page 5
Place-value **N1**
Rounding

a. 1·11 → 1·1   1·11 → 1   **b.** 1·19 → 1·2   1·19 → 1   **c.** 1·33 → 1·3   1·33 → 1
d. 1·45 →1·5   1·45 → 1   **e.** 1·64 → 1·6   1·64 → 2   **f.** 1·99 → 2·0   1·99 → 2
g. 5·08 → 5·1   5·08 → 5   **h.** 5·24 → 5·2   5·24 → 5   **i.** 5·40 → 5·4   5·40 → 5
j. 5·57 → 5·6   5·57 → 6   **k.** 5·78 → 5·8   5·78 → 6   **l.** 5·94 → 5·9   5·94 → 6

1. £9·13 → £9   **2.** £17·12 → £17   **3.** £12·39 → £12   **4.** £7·49 → £7
5. £19·10 → £19   **6.** £15·25 → £15   **7.** £11·32 → £11   **8.** £19·72 → £20
9. £14·91→ £15

1a. £9·13 → £9·10   **2a.** £17·12 → £17·10   **3a.** £12·39 → £12·40
4a. £7·49 → £7·50   **5a.** £19·10 → £19·10   **6a.** £15·25 → £15·30
7a. £11·32 → £11·30   **8a.** £19·72 → £19·70   **9a.** £14·91→ £14·90

1. £20 − £9·13 = £10·87   **2.** £20 − £17·12 = £2·88
3. £20 − £12·39 = £7·61   **4.** £20 − £7·49 = £12·51
5. £20 − £19·10 = £0·90   **6.** £20 − £15·25 = £4·75
7. £20 − £11·32 = £8·68   **8.** £20 − £19·72 = £0·28
9. £20 − £14·91 = £5·09

---

page 6
Place-value **N1**
Rounding

1. 2·24 m → 2·2 m   **2.** 1·79 m → 1·8 m   **3.** 2·15 m → 2·2 m
4. 1·82 m → 1·8 m   **5.** 3·23 m → 3·2 m   **6.** 3·19 m → 3·2 m
7. 3·04 m → 3·0 m   **8.** 4·71 m → 4·7 m   **9.** 2·98 m → 3·0 m
10. 2·95 m → 3·0 m

Number Textbook 1

page 6 cont ...

1a. 2·24 m → 2 m   **2a.** 1·79 m → 2 m   **3a.** 2·15 m → 2 m
4a. 1·82 m → 2 m   **5a.** 3·23 m → 3 m   **6a.** 3·19 m → 3 m
7a. 3·04 m → 3 m   **8a.** 4·71 m → 5 m   **9a.** 2·98 m → 3 m
10a. 2·95 m → 3 m

Explore

Ten possible 1-place decimal numbers which round to 5: 4·5, 4·6, 4·7, 4·8, 4·9, 5·0, 5·1, 5·2, 5·3, 5·4.

Eighty possible 2-place decimal numbers which round to 5:
4·50, 4·51, 4·52, 4·53, 4·56, 4·57, 4·58, 4·59, 4·60, 4·61, 4·62, 4·63, 4·65, 4·67, 4·68, 4·69, 4·70, 4·71, 4·72, 4·73, 4·75, 4·76, 4·78, 4·79, 4·80, 4·81, 4·82, 4·83, 4·85, 4·86, 4·87, 4·89, 4·90, 4·91, 4·92, 4·93, 4·95, 4·96, 4·97, 4·98, 5·01, 5·02, 5·03, 5·04, 5·06, 5·07, 5·08, 5·09, 5·10, 5·12, 5·13, 5·14, 5·16, 5·17, 5·18, 5·19, 5·20, 5·21, 5·23, 5·24, 5·26, 5·27, 5·28, 5·29, 5·30, 5·31, 5·32, 5·34, 5·36, 5·37, 5·38, 5·39, 5·40, 5·41, 5·42, 5·43, 5·46, 5·47, 5·48, 5·49

---

page 7

Dividing by 10

1. 3·1 cm   **2.** 2·2 cm   **3.** 0·7 cm   **4.** 1·3 cm   **5.** 2·9 cm
6. 0·4 cm   **7.** 2·8 cm   **8.** 12·7 cm   **9.** 6 cm   **10.** 4·8 cm

11. $38 \div 10 = 3.8$ **12.** $270 \div 10 = 27$ **13.** $40.6 \times 10 = 406$
14. $4 \div 10 = 0.4^{-}$ **15.** $29 \div 10 = 2.9$ **16.** $118 \div 10 = 11.8$
17. $3562 \div 10 = 356.2$ **18.** $14.7 \times 10 = 147$ **19.** $18 \div 10 = 1.8$
20. $0.9 \times 10 = 9$

@

11a. $3.8 \div 10 = 0.38$ **12a.** $27.0 \div 10 = 2.7$ **13a.** $406 \div 10 = 40.6$
14a. $0.4 \div 10 = 0.04$ **15a.** $2.9 \div 10 = 0.29$ **16a.** $11.8 \div 10 = 1.18$
17a. $356.2 \div 10 = 35.62$ **18a.** $147 \div 10 = 14.7$ **19a.** $1.8 \div 10 = 0.18$
20a. $9 \div 10 = 0.9$

---

page 8

Dividing by 100

1. $248 \div 100 = 2.48$ l   **2.** $144 \div 100 = 1.44$ l   **3.** $399 \div 100 = 3.99$ l
4. $707 \div 100 = 7.07$ l   **5.** $818 \div 100 = 8.18$ l   **6.** $220 \div 100 = 2.2$ l
7. $401 \div 100 = 4.01$ l   **8.** $360 \div 100 = 3.6$ l   **9.** $611 \div 100 = 6.11$ l

Number Textbook 1

1. $2.48 \, l = 2480 \, ml$
2. $1.44 \, l = 1440 \, ml$
3. $3.99 \, l = 3990 \, ml$
4. $7.07 \, l = 7070 \, ml$
5. $8.18 \, l = 8180 \, ml$
6. $2.20 \, l = 2200 \, ml$
7. $4.01 \, l = 4010 \, ml$
8. $3.60 \, l = 3600 \, ml$
9. $6.11 \, l = 6110 \, ml$

10. $341 \div 100 = 3.41$
11. $286 \div 100 = 2.86$
12. $75 \div 100 = 0.75$
13. $11 \div 100 = 0.11$
14. $4.03 \times 100 = 403$
15. $3510 \div 100 = 35.1$
16. $9 \div 100 = 0.09$
17. $40\,350 \div 100 = 403.5$
18. $0.6 \times 100 = 60$
19. $3 \div 100 = 0.03$

page 9
Dividing by 10 and 100

1. $£460 \div £10 = 46$
2. $£6500 \div £100 = 65$
3. $£8600 \div £10 = 860$
4. $£9000 \div £100 = 90$
5. $£4600 \div £100 = 46$
6. $£4600 \div £10 = 460$
7. $£660 \div £10 = 66$
8. $156 \div 10 = 15.6$
9. $148 \div 100 = 1.48$
10. $246 \div 100 = 2.46$
11. $391 \div 100 = 3.91$
12. $14.8 \div 10 = 1.48$
13. $507 \div 100 = 5.07$
14. $786 \div 10 = 78.6$
15. $841 \div 100 = 8.41$
16. $211 \div 100 = 2.11$
17. $929 \div 10 = 92.9$
18. $735 \div 100 = 7.35$
19. $155 \div 10 = 15.5$
20. $232 \div 100 = 2.32$

Explore

When a 3-digit number is divided by 99 the result is a recurring decimal between 1 and 10. Mostly there are two recurring digits e.g. $731 \div 99 = 7.3838383$.

$100 \div 99 = 1.010101$
$101 \div 99 = 1.020202$
$102 \div 99 = 1.030303$
⋮
$197 \div 99 = 1.9898989$
$198 \div 99 = 2$
$199 \div 99 = 2.010101$
⋮
$297 \div 99 = 3$
$298 \div 99 = 3.010101$
⋮
$999 \div 99 = 10.090909$

Number Textbook 1

page 10
Multiplying

1. $6 \times 3 = 18$ eggs
2. $7 \times 6 = 42$ pencils
3. $9 \times 6 = 54$ lollies
4. $9 \times 8 = 72$ candles
5. $8 \times 5 = 40$ balloons
6. $3 \times 7 = 21$ cakes
7. $4 \times 8 = 32$ crackers
8. $7 \times 4 = 28$ pens
9. $8 \times 6 = 48$ stickers
10. $6 \times 9 = 54$ bars

11. $5 \times 9 = 45$ $4 + 5 = 9$
12. $3 \times 9 = 27$ $2 + 7 = 9$
13. $8 \times 9 = 72$ $7 + 2 = 9$
14. $4 \times 9 = 36$ $3 + 6 = 9$
15. $7 \times 9 = 63$ $6 + 3 = 9$
16. $6 \times 9 = 54$ $5 + 4 = 9$
17. $2 \times 9 = 18$ $1 + 8 = 9$
18. $9 \times 9 = 81$ $8 + 1 = 9$

e

$5 \times 18 = 90$ $9 + 0 = 9$ $3 \times 18 = 54$ $5 + 4 = 9$
$8 \times 18 = 144$ $1 + 4 + 4 = 9$ $4 \times 18 = 72$ $7 + 2 = 9$
$7 \times 18 = 126$ $1 + 2 + 6 = 9$ $6 \times 18 = 108$ $1 + 0 + 8 = 9$
$2 \times 18 = 36$ $3 + 6 = 9$ $9 \times 18 = 162$ $1 + 6 + 2 = 9$

---

page 11
Multiplying and dividing

1. $9 \times 5 = 45$ $45 \div 5 = 9$
2. $3 \times 7 = 21$ $21 \div 7 = 3$
3. $2 \times 8 = 16$ $16 \div 8 = 2$
4. $5 \times 6 = 30$ $30 \div 6 = 5$
5. $4 \times 4 = 16$ $16 \div 4 = 4$
6. $8 \times 3 = 24$ $24 \div 3 = 8$
7. $7 \times 4 = 28$ $28 \div 4 = 7$
8. $9 \times 6 = 54$ $54 \div 6 = 9$
9. $8 \times 8 = 64$ $64 \div 8 = 8$
10. $6 \times 6 = 36$ $36 \div 6 = 6$
11. $4 \times 8 = 32$ $32 \div 8 = 4$
12. $8 \times 7 = 56$ $56 \div 7 = 8$
13. $9 \times 4 = 36$ $36 \div 4 = 9$
14. $7 \times 6 = 42$ $42 \div 6 = 7$
15. $7 \times 7 = 49$ $49 \div 7 = 7$
16. $8 \times 6 = 48$ $48 \div 6 = 8$

17. $18 \div 6 = 3$
18. $54 \div 9 = 6$
19. $72 \div 9 = 8$
20. $48 \div 8 = 6$
21. $49 \div 7 = 7$
22. $64 \div 8 = 8$
23. $35 \div 7 = 5$

e

17. $18 \div 5 = 3 \, r \, 3$
18. $54 \div 5 = 10 \, r \, 4$
19. $72 \div 5 = 14 \, r \, 2$
20. $48 \div 5 = 9 \, r \, 3$
21. $49 \div 5 = 9 \, r \, 4$
22. $64 \div 5 = 12 \, r \, 4$
23. $35 \div 5 = 7$

Number Textbook 1

Multiplying and dividing

1. $20 \div 2 = 10$	$25 \div 5 = 5$	$10 > 5$	The girls get more.
2. $27 \div 3 = 9$	$40 \div 4 = 10$	$9 < 10$	The boys get more.
3. $56 \div 8 = 7$	$60 \div 6 = 10$	$7 < 10$	The boys get more.
4. $42 \div 6 = 7$	$24 \div 8 = 3$	$7 > 3$	The girls get more.
5. $64 \div 8 = 8$	$49 \div 7 = 7$	$8 > 7$	The girls get more.
6. $36 \div 6 = 6$	$70 \div 7 = 10$	$6 < 10$	The boys get more.
7. $48 \div 6 = 8$	$6 \div 1 = 6$	$8 > 6$	The girls get more.
8. $12 \div 2 = 6$	$35 \div 7 = 5$	$6 > 5$	The girls get more.
9. $63 \div 9 = 7$	$28 \div 4 = 7$	$7 = 7$	They get the same.
10. $35 \div 5 = 7$	$54 \div 9 = 6$	$7 > 6$	The girls get more.

11. $30 \div 5 = 6$ 12. $42 \div 7 = 6$ 13. $36 \div 6 = 6$ 14. $70 \div 10 = 7$
15. $48 \div 8 = 6$ 16. $32 \div 4 = 8$ 17. $63 \div 9 = 7$ 18. $18 \div 2 = 9$
19. $56 \div 7 = 8$ 20. $35 \div 5 = 7$

Explore

2 divides into 2, 12, 20, 22, 24, 26, 28, 32, 42, 52, …
3 divides into 3, 30, 33, 36, 39, 63, 93, …
4 divides into 4, 24, 40, 44, 48, 64, 84, 104, …
5 divides into 5, 15, 25, 35, 45, 50, 55, 65, …
6 divides into 6, 36, 60, 66, 96, 126, …
7 divides into 7, 70, 77, 147, …
8 divides into 8, 48, 80, 88, 128, …
9 divides into 9, 90, 99, 189, …
30 pairs with the second number less than 50.

Multiplying and dividing

1. $3 \times 8 = 24$ 2. $6 \times 6 = 36$ 3. $4 \times 8 = 32$ 4. $7 \times 6 = 42$
5. $6 \times 9 = 54$ 6. $6 \times 8 = 48$ 7. $8 \times 7 = 56$ 8. $7 \times 7 = 49$
9. $8 \times 9 = 72$ 10. $7 \times 4 = 28$

11. $72 \div 12 = 6$ It is 6 miles from Georgie's house to work.
12. $42 \div 6 = 7$ Callum uses 7 pages.
    $6 \times 5 = 30$ He can stick 30 more photos in the album.
13. $45 \div 3 = 15$ Sam can fit 15 songs on the tape.
    $15 \div 3 = 5$ He could fit 5 more songs on a 60-minute tape.

Number Textbook 1

14. £8·40 ÷ 20p = 42   42 days = 6 weeks   It takes Yasmin 42 days to save enough money.
15. 248 g ÷ 8 = 31 g   Each cake weighs 31 g.   31 g × 33 = 1023 g = 1·023 kg 33 cakes would weigh just over 1 kg.
16. $1\frac{1}{2}$ minutes = 90 seconds   90 ÷ 3 = 30   The fan makes 30 turns.

page 14
Doubling and halving

1. $\frac{1}{2}$ of 84 = 42   Sharks 42 baskets $\frac{1}{2}$ of 72 = 36   Rockets 36 baskets
2. $\frac{1}{2}$ of 58 = 29   Hawks 29 baskets $\frac{1}{2}$ of 48 = 24   Hornets 24 baskets
3. $\frac{1}{2}$ of 56 = 28   Bulls 28 baskets $\frac{1}{2}$ of 98 = 49   Warriors 49 baskets
4. $\frac{1}{2}$ of 118 = 59   Wolves 59 baskets $\frac{1}{2}$ of 76 = 38   Royals 38 baskets
5. $\frac{1}{2}$ of 104 = 52   Kings 52 baskets $\frac{1}{2}$ of 94 = 47   Blazers 47 baskets
6. $\frac{1}{2}$ of 126 = 63   Pistons 63 baskets $\frac{1}{2}$ of 68 = 34   Mavericks 34 baskets

1. Sharks 106   Rockets 94   2. Hawks 80   Hornets 70
3. Bulls 78   Warriors 120   4. Wolves 140   Royals 98
5. Kings 126   Blazers 116   6. Pistons 148   Mavericks 90

7. double 46 = 80 + 12 = 92 points   8. double 72 = 140 + 4 = 144 points
9. double 39 = 60 + 18 = 78 points   10. double 57 = 100 + 14 = 114 points
11. double 69 = 120 + 18 = 138 points   12. double 77 = 140 + 14 = 154 points
13. double 28 = 40 + 16 = 56 points   14. double 86 = 160 + 12 = 172 points

7. Dead-eye Dave 46 − 13 = 33   8. Top-shot Tess 72 − 13 = 59
9. Hawk-eye Helen 39 − 13 = 26   10. Magic Mike 57 − 13 = 44
11. Handy Andy 69 − 13 = 56   12. Careful Connie 77 − 13 = 64
13. Speedy Seb 28 − 13 = 15   14. Lightning Lil 86 − 13 = 73

page 15
Doubling and halving

1. half of £320 = £160   2. half of £640 = £320   3. half of £560 = £280
4. half of £180 = £90   5. half of £760 = £380   6. half of £840 = £420
7. half of £430 = £215   8. half of £670 = £335   9. half of £980 = £490

Number Textbook 1

1. half of £160 = £80   **2.** half of £320 = £160   **3.** half of £280 = £140
4. half of £90 = £45   **5.** half of £380 = £190   **6.** half of £420 = £210
7. half of £215 = £107·50   **8.** half of £335 = £167·50   **9.** half of £490 = £245

10. double £2600 = £5200   **11.** double £4300 = £8600
12. double £9400 = £18 800   **13.** double £3200 = £6400
14. double £1700 = £3400   **15.** double £4500 = £9000
16. double £6700 = £13 400   **17.** double £8300 = £16 600
18. double £3900 = £7800

---

page 16
Doubling and halving

1. double 3·4 km = 6·8 km   **2.** double 2·5 km = 5 km
3. double 2·8 km = 5·6 km   **4.** double 3·9 km = 7·8 km
5. double 2·8 km = 5·6 km   **6.** double 5·6 km = 11·2 km
7. double 1·9 km = 3·8 km   **8.** double 6·9 km = 13·8 km
9. double 4·1 km = 8·2 km   **10.** double 1·7 km = 3·4 km
11. half of 12·6 km = 6·3 km   **12.** half of 8·8 km = 4·4 km
13. half of 9·4 km = 4·7 km   **14.** half of 4·8 km = 2·4 km
15. half of 5·6 km = 2·8 km   **16.** half of 18·8 km = 9·4 km
17. half of 11·8 km = 5·9 km   **18.** half of 17·4 km = 8·7 km

Explore

Assuming one set of cards 1 to 9.
The first number must lie between 500 and 990. Possibilities are:

640 and 1280	670 and 1340	690 and 1380
730 and 1460	760 and 1520	780 and 1560
790 and 1580	820 and 1640	860 and 1720
920 and 1840	930 and 1860	

All other pairs require a repeated digit.

---

page 17
Multiplying by nearly 50

1. £62 × 49 = £3038   **2.** £83 × 49 = £4067   **3.** £24 × 49 = £1176
4. £49 × 49 = £2401   **5.** £42 × 49 = £2058   **6.** £53 × 49 = £2597
7. £27 × 49 = £1323   **8.** £35 × 49 = £1715   **9.** £42 × 49 = £2058
10. £29 × 49 = £1421   **11.** £64 × 49 = £3136   **12.** £57 × 49 = £2793

Number Textbook 1

@

1. £62 × 98 = £6076
2. £83 × 98 = £8134
3. £24 × 98 = £2352
4. £49 × 98 = £4802
5. £42 × 98 = £4116
6. £53 × 98 = £5194
7. £27 × 98 = £2646
8. £35 × 98 = £3430
9. £42 × 98 = £4116
10. £29 × 98 = £2842
11. £64 × 98 = £6272
12. £57 × 98 = £5586

13. 43p × 51 = 2193p = £21·93
14. 62p × 51 = 3162p = £31·62
15. 35p × 51 = 1785 = £17·85
16. 47p × 51 = 2397p = £23·97
17. 28p × 51 = 1428p = £14·28
18. 54p × 51 = 2754p = £27·54
19. 37p × 51 = 1887p = £18·87
20. 74p × 51 = 3774p = £37·74
21. 83p × 51 = 4233p = £42·33

Multiplying by nearly 100

1. 38 × 99 = 3762   36 × 101 = 3636   99 rows of 38 has more seats
2. 33 × 99 = 3267   27 × 101 = 2727   99 rows of 33 has more seats
3. 54 × 99 = 5346   52 × 101 = 5252   99 rows of 54 has more seats
4. 23 × 99 = 2277   17 × 101 = 1717   99 rows of 23 has more seats
5. 82 × 99 = 8118   78 × 101 = 7878   99 rows of 82 has more seats
6. 31 × 99 = 3069   28 × 101 = 2828   99 rows of 31 has more seats
7. 67 × 99 = 6633   54 × 101 = 5454   99 rows of 67 has more seats

@

1. 3762 – 3636 = 126
2. 3267 – 2727 = 540
3. 5346 – 5252 = 94
4. 2277 – 1717 = 560
5. 8118 – 7878 = 240
6. 3069 – 2828 = 241
7. 6633 – 5454 = 1179

Explore

76 × 101 = 7676   34 × 101 = 3434   85 × 101 = 8585
76 × 1001 = 76076   34 × 1001 = 34034   85 × 1001 = 85085

51 × 101 = 5151   12 × 101 = 1212
51 × 1001 = 51051   12 × 1001 = 12012

If the digits of the 2-digit number are ab, then ab × 101 = abab,
ab × 1001 = ab0ab

For a 3-digit number abc, then abc × 101 = ab(a+c)bc

If a and c total 9 or less then this is straightforward:
e.g. 276 × 101 = 27876.
If a and c total more than 9, then a digit must be carried:
e.g. 489 × 101 = 49 389.

Number Textbook 1

Multiplying

1. $48 \times 82 = 3936$ 2. $102 \times 39 = 3978$ 3. $47 \times 83 = 3901$
4. $52 \times 78 = 4056$ 5. $98 \times 42 = 4116$ 6. $97 \times 44 = 4268$
7. $51 \times 79 = 4029$ 8. $103 \times 37 = 3811$ 9. $99 \times 41 = 4059$

Three closest are 102×39, 51×79, 52×78.

  1. $4000 - 3936 = 64$ 2. $4000 - 3978 = 22$ 3. $4000 - 3901 = 99$
4. $4056 - 4000 = 56$ 5. $4116 - 4000 = 116$ 6. $4268 - 4000 = 268$
7. $4029 - 4000 = 29$ 8. $4000 - 3811 = 189$ 9. $4059 - 4000 = 59$

10. $48 \text{ cm} \times 18 = 864 \text{ cm} = 8.64 \text{ m}$ Amelia's hall is 8·64 m long.
11. $£98.99 \times 24 = £2375.76$ The shop makes £2375·76.
12. $250 \text{ g} \times 101 = 25\,250 \text{ g} = 25.25 \text{ kg per day}$
    $25.25 \text{ kg} \times 7 = 176.75 \text{ kg}$ Dotty needs 176·75 kg of dog food each week.

Multiplying by doubling

1. $3 \times 8 = 24$ $3 \times 16 = 48$ $3 \times 32 = 96$
2. $5 \times 7 = 35$ $5 \times 14 = 70$ $5 \times 28 = 140$
3. $4 \times 9 = 36$ $4 \times 18 = 72$ $4 \times 36 = 144$
4. $7 \times 6 = 42$ $7 \times 12 = 84$ $7 \times 24 = 168$
5. $3 \times 7 = 21$ $3 \times 14 = 42$ $3 \times 28 = 84$

6. $£16 \times 13 = £208$ 7. $£16 \times 24 = £384$ 8. $£16 \times 11 = £176$
9. $£16 \times 31 = £496$ 10. $£18 \times 12 = £216$ 11. $£18 \times 20 = £360$
12. $£18 \times 35 = £630$ 13. $£18 \times 23 = £414$ 14. $£28 \times 17 = £476$
15. $£28 \times 21 = £588$ 16. $£28 \times 33 = £924$ 17. $£28 \times 42 = £1176$

Multiplying by doubling and halving

1. $18 \times 15 = 270$ 2. $8 \times 32 = 256$ 3. $16 \times 29 = 464$
4. $12 \times 23 = 276$ 5. $11 \times 14 = 154$ 6. $36 \times 25 = 900$
7. $32 \times 13 = 416$ 8. $21 \times 48 = 1008$ 9. $12 \times 44 = 528$
10. $30 \times 32 = 960$ 11. $28 \times 36 = 1008$ 12. $24 \times 15 = 360$
13. $44 \times 25 = 1100$ 14. $51 \times 16 = 816$ 15. $18 \times 32 = 576$
16. $24 \times 22 = 528$

Number Textbook 1

17. $15 \times 24p = 360p = £3·60$ **18.** $26 \times 35p = 910p = £9·10$
19. $45 \times 28p = 1260p = £12·60$ **20.** $25 \times 32p = 800p = £8·00$
21. $28 \times 25p = 700p = £7·00$ **22.** $42 \times 35p = 1470p = £14·70$
23. $75 \times 24p = 1800p = £18·00$ **24.** $34 \times 25p = 850p = £8·50$
25. $35 \times 28p = 980p = £9·80$

Multiplying by 25

1. 25 seconds $\times$ 24 = 600 seconds   **1a.** 10 minutes
2. 25 seconds $\times$ 36 = 900 seconds   **2a.** 15 minutes
3. 25 seconds $\times$ 18 = 450 seconds   **3a.** 7 minutes 30 seconds
4. 25 seconds $\times$ 12 = 300 seconds   **4a.** 5 minutes
5. 25 seconds $\times$ 48 = 1200 seconds   **5a.** 20 minutes
6. 25 seconds $\times$ 28 = 700 seconds   **6a.** 11 minutes 40 seconds
7. 25 seconds $\times$ 96 = 2400 seconds   **7a.** 40 minutes
8. 25 seconds $\times$ 34 = 850 seconds   **8a.** 14 minutes 10 seconds
9. 25 seconds $\times$ 26 = 650 seconds   **9a.** 10 minutes 50 seconds

10. 42 seats $\times$ 25 = 1050 seats $1134 - 1050 = 84$ 84 people have to stand.
11. 25 slices $\times$ 38 = 950 slices $950 > 900$ Yes, there is enough ham.
12. $£12·20 \times 25 = £305$ The total cost is £305.
13. $£39 \times 25 = £975$ $£1000 - £975 = £25$ There is £25 change.

Finding fractions of quantities

1. $\frac{1}{6}$ of 24 = 4   **2.** $\frac{1}{5}$ of 35 = 7   **3.** $\frac{1}{9}$ of 36 = 4
4. $\frac{1}{10}$ of 100 = 10   **5.** $\frac{1}{4}$ of 40 = 10   **6.** $\frac{1}{8}$ of 32 = 4
7. $\frac{1}{7}$ of 28 = 4   **8.** $\frac{7}{8}$ of 32 = 28   **9.** $\frac{3}{5}$ of 25 = 15
10. $\frac{4}{7}$ of 28 = 16   **11.** $\frac{2}{3}$ of 60 = 40   **12.** $\frac{3}{10}$ of 140 = 42
13. $\frac{3}{4}$ of 44 = 33   **14.** $\frac{5}{6}$ of 180 = 150   **15.** $\frac{8}{9}$ of 72 = 64
16. $\frac{4}{11}$ of 121 = 44

Number Textbook 1

Finding fractions of quantities

1. $\frac{4}{10}$ of £125 = £50   2. $\frac{4}{10}$ of £58 = £23·20   3. $\frac{4}{10}$ of £12·50 = £5·00

4. $\frac{4}{10}$ of £150 = £60   5. $\frac{4}{10}$ of £425 = £170   6. $\frac{4}{10}$ of £260 = £104

7. $\frac{4}{10}$ of £320 = £128   8. $\frac{4}{10}$ of £740 = £296   9. $\frac{4}{10}$ of £1000 = £400

✐ £50 + £23·20 + £5 + £60 + £170 + £104 + £128 + £296 + £400 = £1236·20

10. $\frac{4}{5}$ of 40 = 32   11. $\frac{7}{8}$ of 48 = 42   12. $\frac{2}{9}$ of 81 = 18

13. $\frac{2}{7}$ of 77 = 22   14. $\frac{3}{4}$ of 28 = 21   15. $\frac{2}{3}$ of 90 = 60

16. $\frac{5}{6}$ of 120 = 100   17. $\frac{3}{8}$ of 240 = 90   18. $\frac{7}{10}$ of 500 = 350

Finding fractions of quantities

1. $\frac{3}{8}$ of £3·20 = £1·20   2. $\frac{4}{5}$ of £4·00 = £3·20   3. $\frac{3}{4}$ of £4·80 = £3·60

4. $\frac{4}{10}$ of £1·70 = 68p   5. $\frac{2}{7}$ of £2·80 = 80p   6. $\frac{3}{8}$ of £5·60 = £2·10

7. $\frac{5}{12}$ of £2·40 = £1·00   8. $\frac{2}{25}$ of £5 = 40p   9. $\frac{7}{9}$ of £4·50 = £3·50

10. 56 − 16 = 40 $\frac{40}{56} = \frac{5}{7}$

11. $\frac{3}{8}$ of 24 m = 9 m $\frac{1}{6}$ of 24 m = 4 m   24 − (9 + 4) = 11 m $\frac{1}{2}$ of 11 = 5·5 m

12. $\frac{30}{120} = \frac{1}{4}$ $\frac{20}{120} = \frac{1}{6}$ $\frac{15}{120} = \frac{1}{8}$ 120 − (30 + 20 + 15) = 55 left $\frac{55}{120} = \frac{11}{24}$

Equivalent fractions

1.–12. Answers will vary.

✐ Answers will vary.

13. $\frac{5}{20} = \frac{1}{4}$ 14. $\frac{3}{15} = \frac{1}{5}$ 15. $\frac{6}{18} = \frac{1}{3}$ 16. $\frac{10}{80} = \frac{1}{8}$ 17. $\frac{7}{63} = \frac{1}{9}$

18. $\frac{9}{72} = \frac{1}{8}$ 19. $\frac{24}{64} = \frac{3}{8}$ 20. $\frac{27}{90} = \frac{3}{10}$ 21. $\frac{16}{36} = \frac{4}{9}$ 22. $\frac{30}{45} = \frac{2}{3}$

✐ Answers will vary.

Number Textbook 1

Equivalent fractions

1. $\frac{27}{36} = \frac{3}{4}$ 2. $\frac{15}{20} = \frac{3}{4}$ 3. $\frac{4}{14} = \frac{2}{7}$ 4. $\frac{8}{20} = \frac{2}{5}$ 5. $\frac{6}{9} = \frac{2}{3}$

6. $\frac{12}{42} = \frac{2}{7}$ 7. $\frac{27}{45} = \frac{3}{5}$ 8. $\frac{70}{100} = \frac{7}{10}$ 9. $\frac{16}{36} = \frac{4}{9}$

10. $\frac{16}{24} = \frac{2}{3}$ 11. $\frac{12}{24} = \frac{1}{2}$ 12. $\frac{18}{24} = \frac{3}{4}$ 13. $\frac{12}{24} = \frac{1}{2}$ 14. $\frac{4}{24} = \frac{1}{6}$

15. $\frac{9}{24} = \frac{3}{8}$ 16. $\frac{4}{24} = \frac{1}{6}$ 17. $\frac{7}{24}$

Equivalent fractions

1. $\frac{6}{9} = \frac{2}{3}$ $\frac{2}{3}$ of £30 = £20   2. $\frac{6}{15} = \frac{2}{5}$ $\frac{2}{5}$ of £40 = £16

3. $\frac{15}{20} = \frac{3}{4}$ $\frac{3}{4}$ of £24 = £18   4. $\frac{8}{16} = \frac{1}{2}$ $\frac{1}{2}$ of £4 = £2

5. $\frac{24}{32} = \frac{3}{4}$ $\frac{3}{4}$ of £16 = £12   6. $\frac{32}{40} = \frac{4}{5}$ $\frac{4}{5}$ of £10 = £8

7. $\frac{9}{21} = \frac{3}{7}$ $\frac{3}{7}$ of £7 = £3   8. $\frac{36}{81} = \frac{4}{9}$ $\frac{4}{9}$ of £18 = £8

Explore

$\frac{1}{3}$ of 24 = 8 $\frac{1}{4}$ of 32 = 8 $\frac{1}{5}$ of 40 = 8 $\frac{1}{6}$ of 48 = 8 $\frac{1}{7}$ of 56 = 8

$\frac{1}{8}$ of 64 = 8 $\frac{1}{9}$ of 72 = 8

$\frac{2}{4}$ of 16 = 8 $\frac{2}{9}$ of 36 = 8

$\frac{3}{9}$ of 24 = 8 $\frac{4}{6}$ of 12 = 8 $\frac{4}{8}$ of 16 = 8 $\frac{6}{9}$ of 12 = 8

Assuming that the fractions are proper, i.e. the numerator is less than the denominator, and each card can only be used once, then 13 arrangements are possible.

Converting fractions

a. $\frac{1}{2} = \frac{12}{24}$ b. $\frac{2}{3} = \frac{16}{24}$ c. $\frac{5}{6} = \frac{20}{24}$ d. $\frac{1}{3} = \frac{8}{24}$ e. $\frac{3}{4} = \frac{18}{24}$

f. $\frac{1}{6} = \frac{4}{24}$ g. $\frac{1}{4} = \frac{6}{24}$ h. $\frac{1}{12} = \frac{2}{24}$ i. $\frac{5}{12} = \frac{10}{24}$ j. $\frac{11}{12} = \frac{22}{24}$

A number line from 0 to 1, marked at:
0 $\frac{2}{24}$ $\frac{4}{24}$ $\frac{6}{24}$ $\frac{8}{24}$ $\frac{10}{24}$ $\frac{12}{24}$ $\frac{14}{24}$ $\frac{16}{24}$ $\frac{18}{24}$ $\frac{20}{24}$ $\frac{22}{24}$ 1

Number Textbook 1

1. $\frac{3}{5} = \frac{9}{15}$ $\frac{2}{3} = \frac{10}{15}$ $\frac{3}{5} < \frac{2}{3}$ 2. $\frac{2}{3} = \frac{8}{12}$ $\frac{3}{4} = \frac{9}{12}$ $\frac{2}{3} < \frac{3}{4}$

3. $\frac{3}{4} = \frac{15}{20}$ $\frac{4}{5} = \frac{16}{20}$ $\frac{3}{4} < \frac{4}{5}$ 4. $\frac{5}{6} = \frac{15}{18}$ $\frac{7}{9} = \frac{14}{18}$ $\frac{5}{6} > \frac{7}{9}$

5. $\frac{3}{4} = \frac{21}{28}$ $\frac{5}{7} = \frac{20}{28}$ $\frac{3}{4} > \frac{5}{7}$ 6. $\frac{5}{12} = \frac{35}{84}$ $\frac{3}{7} = \frac{36}{84}$ $\frac{5}{12} < \frac{3}{7}$

7. $\frac{4}{5} = \frac{36}{45}$ $\frac{5}{9} = \frac{25}{45}$ $\frac{4}{5} > \frac{5}{9}$

Ordering fractions

1. $\frac{2}{3} = \frac{40}{60}$ $\frac{3}{5} = \frac{36}{60}$ $\frac{3}{4} = \frac{45}{60}$ $\frac{3}{5} < \frac{2}{3} < \frac{3}{4}$

2. $\frac{2}{7} = \frac{6}{21}$ $\frac{1}{3} = \frac{7}{21}$ $\frac{8}{21}$ $\frac{2}{7} < \frac{1}{3} < \frac{8}{21}$

3. $\frac{5}{9} = \frac{10}{18}$ $\frac{2}{3} = \frac{12}{18}$ $\frac{11}{18}$ $\frac{5}{9} < \frac{11}{18} < \frac{2}{3}$

4. $\frac{1}{4} = \frac{3}{12}$ $\frac{5}{12}$ $\frac{2}{3} = \frac{8}{12}$ $\frac{1}{4} < \frac{5}{12} < \frac{2}{3}$

5. $\frac{3}{5} = \frac{42}{70}$ $\frac{1}{2} = \frac{35}{70}$ $\frac{4}{7} = \frac{40}{70}$ $\frac{1}{2} < \frac{4}{7} < \frac{3}{5}$

6. $\frac{3}{4} = \frac{15}{20}$ $\frac{4}{5} = \frac{16}{20}$ $\frac{7}{10} = \frac{14}{20}$ $\frac{7}{10} < \frac{3}{4} < \frac{4}{5}$

7. $\frac{1}{2} = \frac{6}{12}$ $\frac{7}{12}$ $\frac{5}{6} = \frac{10}{12}$ $\frac{1}{2} < \frac{7}{12} < \frac{5}{6}$

8. $\frac{3}{7} = \frac{27}{63}$ $\frac{2}{3} = \frac{42}{63}$ $\frac{4}{9} = \frac{28}{63}$ $\frac{3}{7} < \frac{4}{9} < \frac{2}{3}$

9. $\frac{1}{2} = \frac{33}{66}$ $\frac{1}{3} = \frac{22}{66}$ $\frac{5}{11} = \frac{30}{66}$ $\frac{1}{3} < \frac{5}{11} < \frac{1}{2}$

10. $\frac{9}{10} = \frac{54}{60}$ $\frac{3}{4} = \frac{45}{60}$ $\frac{11}{12} = \frac{55}{60}$ $\frac{3}{4} < \frac{9}{10} < \frac{11}{12}$

11. $\frac{2}{3} = \frac{80}{120}$ $\frac{4}{5} = \frac{96}{120}$ $\frac{5}{8} = \frac{75}{120}$ $\frac{5}{8} < \frac{2}{3} < \frac{4}{5}$

🌚 Answers will vary.

Explore

$\frac{1}{3}, \frac{2}{5}, \frac{3}{7}, \frac{3}{8}, \frac{4}{9}, \frac{4}{10}, \frac{4}{11}, \frac{5}{11}, \frac{5}{12}, \frac{5}{13}, \frac{6}{13}, \frac{5}{14}, \frac{6}{14}, \frac{6}{15}, \frac{5}{15}, \frac{6}{16}, \frac{7}{16}, \frac{6}{17}, \frac{7}{17}, \frac{7}{17}, \frac{6}{18}, \frac{7}{18}, \frac{8}{18}, \frac{7}{19}, \frac{8}{19}, \frac{9}{19}$

Finding the mid-point between fractions

1. $2\frac{3}{7} = 2\frac{6}{14}$ $2\frac{4}{7} = 2\frac{8}{14}$ mid-point: $2\frac{7}{14} = 2\frac{1}{2}$

2. $3\frac{3}{5} = 3\frac{6}{10}$ $3\frac{4}{5} = 3\frac{8}{10}$ mid-point: $3\frac{7}{10}$

3. $1\frac{1}{3} = 1\frac{2}{6}$ $1\frac{2}{3} = 1\frac{4}{6}$ mid-point: $1\frac{3}{6} = 1\frac{1}{2}$

4. $2\frac{4}{7} = 2\frac{8}{14}$ $2\frac{5}{7} = 2\frac{10}{14}$ mid-point: $2\frac{9}{14}$

5. mid-point: $1\frac{4}{8} = 1\frac{1}{2}$

6. $4\frac{7}{9} = 4\frac{14}{18}$ $4\frac{8}{9} = 4\frac{16}{18}$ mid-point: $4\frac{15}{18} = 4\frac{5}{6}$

Number Textbook 1

7. $3\frac{6}{11} = 3\frac{12}{22}$ $3\frac{7}{11} = 3\frac{14}{22}$ mid-point: $3\frac{13}{22}$

8. $5\frac{13}{15} = 5\frac{26}{30}$ $5\frac{14}{15} = 5\frac{28}{30}$ mid-point: $4\frac{27}{30} = 4\frac{9}{10}$

9. mid-point: 7

10. $\frac{3}{4}$ of 16 = 12 $(12 \div 2) \times 5 = 30$

11. $\frac{1}{3}$ of 18 = 6 $(6 \div 3) \times 8 = 16$

12. $\frac{1}{2}$ of 24 = 12 $(12 \div 4) \times 7 = 21$

13. $\frac{1}{8}$ of 64 = 8 $(8 \div 8) \times 15 = 15$

14. $\frac{6}{7}$ of 63 = 54 $(54 \div 9) \times 10 = 60$

15. $\frac{2}{3}$ of 330 = 220 $(220 \div 11) \times 12 = 240$

---

page 32   Addition/subtraction   N10
Adding to make 10 and 100

1. 46 + 54 = 100   2. 35 + 65 = 100   3. 72 + 28 = 100
4. 66 + 34 = 100   5. 53 + 47 = 100   6. 64 + 36 = 100
7. 23 + 77 = 100   8. 29 + 71 = 100   9. 34 + 66 = 100
10. 88 + 12 = 100   11. 51 + 49 = 100   12. 17 + 83 = 100
13. 94 + 6 = 100   14. 83 + 17 = 100

15. 3·8 m + 6·2 m = 10 m   6·2 m further
16. 4·2 m + 5·8 m = 10 m   5·8 m further
17. 6·7 m + 3·3 m = 10 m   3·3 m further
18. 9·8 m + 0·2 m = 10 m   0·2 m further
19. 1·4 m + 8·6 m = 10 m   8·6 m further
20. 5·3 m + 4·7 m = 10 m   4·7 m further
21. 2·9 m + 7·1 m = 10 m   7·1 m further
22. 7·1 m + 2·9 m = 10 m   2·9 m further
23. 8·5 m + 1·5 m = 10 m   1·5 m further

---

page 33   Addition/subtraction   N10
Adding to make 10 and 100

1. £9·36 + £0·64 = £10   change 64p
2. £9·18 + £0·82 = £10   change 82p
3. £7·79 + £2·21 = £10   change £2·21
4. £5·54 + £4·46 = £10   change £4·46
5. £6·38 + £3·62 = £10   change £3·62
6. £7·62 + £2·38 = £10   change £2·38

Number Textbook 1

7. £8·81 + £1·19 = £10   change £1·19
8. £4·01 + £5·99 = £10   change £5·99
9. £5·27 + £4·73 = £10   change £4·73
10. £3·49 + £6·51 = £10   change £6·51
11. £6·91 + £3·09 = £10   change £3·09

12. 42 + 58 = 100   420 + 580 = 1000   420 + 80 = 500
    42 + 8 = 50   4·2 + 5·8 = 10   4·2 + 0·8 = 5
13. 73 + 27 = 100   730 + 270 = 1000   73 + 427 = 500
    7·3 + 42·7 = 50   7·3 + 2·7 = 10   0·73 + 4·27 = 5
14. 81 + 19 = 100   810 + 190 = 1000   81 + 419 = 500
    8·1 + 41·9 = 50   8·1 + 1·9 = 10   0·81 + 4·19 = 5
15. 46 + 54 = 100   460 + 540 = 1000   460 + 40 = 500
    46 + 4 = 50   4·6 + 5·4 = 10   4·6 + 0·4 = 5
16. 34 + 66 = 100   340 + 660 = 1000   340 + 160 = 500
    34 + 16 = 50   3·4 + 6·6 = 10   3·4 + 1·6 = 5
17. 27 + 73 = 100   270 + 730 = 1000   270 + 230 = 500
    27 + 23 = 50   2·7 + 7·3 = 10   2·7 + 2·3 = 5
18. 58 + 42 = 100   580 + 420 = 1000   58 + 442 = 500
    5·8 + 44·2 = 50   5·8 + 4·2 = 10   0·58 + 4·42 = 5
19. 85 + 15 = 100   850 + 150 = 1000   85 + 415 = 500
    8·5 + 41·5 = 50   8·5 + 1·5 = 10   0·85 + 4·15 = 5
20. 19 + 81 = 100   190 + 810 = 1000   190 + 310 = 500
    19 + 31 = 50   1·9 + 8·1 = 10   1·9 + 3·1 = 5
21. 93 + 7 = 100   930 + 70 = 1000   93 + 407 = 500
    93 + 7 = 100   9·3 + 0·7 = 10   0·93 + 4·07 = 5

Adding to make multiples of 100

1. 370 + 130 = 500   130 km further
2. 460 + 340 = 800   340 km further
3. 520 + 380 = 900   380 km further
4. 660 + 40 = 700   40 km further
5. 290 + 710 = 1000   710 km further
6. 140 + 260 = 400   260 km further
7. 730 + 570 = 1300   570 km further
8. 940 + 760 = 1700   760 km further
9. 350 + 1150 = 1500   1150 km further
10. 810 + 290 = 1100   290 km further

Number Textbook 1

page 34 cont ...
Explore

There are 44 pairs of 3-digit multiples of 10 with a difference of 270.

370, 100	390, 120	400, 130	420, 150	430, 160	450, 180
460, 190	470, 200	480, 210	500, 230	510, 240	530, 260
540, 270	560, 290	570, 300	580, 310	590, 320	610, 340
620, 350	640, 370	650, 380	670, 400	680, 410	690, 420
700, 430	720, 450	730, 460	750, 480	760, 490	780, 510
790, 520	800, 530	810, 540	830, 560	840, 570	860, 590
870, 600	890, 620	900, 630	910, 640	920, 650	940, 670
950, 680	980, 710				

---

page 35
Adding decimals

1. $15.7 + 2.7 = 18.4$ 2.7 l needed
2. $12.9 + 6.6 = 19.5$ 6.6 l needed
3. $14.8 + 2.5 = 17.3$ 2.5 l needed
4. $11.6 + 3.6 = 15.2$ 3.6 l needed
5. $13.1 + 4.9 = 18.0$ 4.9 l needed
6. $16.4 + 4.1 = 20.5$ 4.1 l needed
7. $19.7 + 2.6 = 22.3$ 2.6 l needed

@

1. 2.7 litres = 2700 ml = 270 cl
2. 6.6 litres = 6600 ml = 660 cl
3. 2.5 litres = 2500 ml = 250 cl
3. 3.6 litres = 3600 ml = 360 cl
5. 4.9 litres = 4900 ml = 490 cl
4. 4.1 litres = 4100 ml = 410 cl
7. 2.6 litres = 2600 ml = 260 cl

8. $10 m - (5.4 m + 1.61 m) = 2.99 m$ There are 2.99 m of string left.
9. $10m - 3.5 m = 6.5 m = 650 cm$ $650 cm \div 50 cm = 13$
The tree takes 13 months to grow.
10. $5 kg - 4.62 kg = 0.38 kg = 380 g$ The puppy must gain 380 g.
11. $26.25 miles - 17.5 miles = 8.75 miles$ She must go 8.75 miles further.
12. $£6 - £4.63 = £1.37$ Simon must borrow £1.37.
13. $£5 - (£0.90 + £2.87) = £1.23$ Anya gets £1.23 change.

---

page 36
Adding

1. $85p + 79p + 64p + 58p = 286p = £2.86$
2. $99p + 39p + 45p + 89p = 272p = £2.72$
3. $69p + 49p + 55p + 75p = 248p = £2.48$
4. $99p + 75 + 27p + 61p = 262p = £2.62$
5. $46p + 52p + 87p + 91p = 276p = £2.76$

Number Textbook 1

page 36 cont ...

6. 63p + 47p + 39p + 90p = 239p = £2·39
7. 18p + 78p + 59p + 96p = 251p = £2·51
8. 36p + 49p + 71p + 68p = 224p = £2·24
9. 52p + 33p + 77p + 28p = 190p = £1·90
10. 11p + 99p + 74p + 47p = 231p = £2·31

1. £5 – £2·86 = £2·14   2. £5 – £2·72 = £2·28   3. £5 – £2·48 = £2·52
4. £5 – £2·62 = £2·38   5. £5 – £2·76 = £2·24   6. £5 – £2·39 = £2·61
7. £5 – £2·51 = £2·49   8. £5 – £2·24 = £2·76   9. £5 – £1·90 = £3·10
10. £5 – £2·31 = £2·69

11. £145 – £99 = £46   £46 – £2·99 = £43·01
12. £204 – £99 = £105   £105 – £4·99 = £100·01
13. £149 – £99 = £50   £50 – £5·99 = £44·01
14. £250 – £99 = £151   £151 – £9·99 = £141·01
15. £113 – £99 = £14   £14 – £3·59 = £10·41
16. £220 – £99 = £121   £121 – £3·33 = £117·67

---

page 37
Adding

1. 28 + 35 + 23 – 19 = 67
2. 18 + 21 – 9 + 19 – 17 = 32
3. 14 + 29 – 18 – 7 + 19 = 37
4. 22 – 19 + 29 – 18 = 14
5. 24 – 9 + 17 – 12 = 20
6. 31 – 19 + 13 + 29 = 54
7. 11 + 38 – 29 – 20 = 0
8. 87 – 29 + 7 = 65   65 – 55 = 10

The director must cut 10 minutes of film.

9. 48 – 19 – 27 = 2   2 ÷ 2 = 1
10. 89 + 27 – 11 = 105
Ricky arrives at 11:45 a.m.

Jamal and Harriet get 1 plant each.
105 minutes = 1 hour 45 minutes.

---

page 38
Adding

1. 87 + 29 + 37 = 153   153 pages
2. 111 – 19 + 37 + 25 = 154   154 pages
3. 204 – 87 + 29 – 35 + 42 = 153   153 pages
4. 347 – 98 + 117 + 219 = 585 585 g
5. 399 – 86 + 134 + 122 = 569 569 g
6. 407 – 76 + 121 – 46 + 237 = 643   643 g

Number Textbook 1

page 38 cont ...

7. £2·24 − £0·99 + £4·50 − £1·65 = £4·10
8. £3·01 − £0·78 − £1·57 + £3·50 = £4·16
9. £5·84 + £2·50 − £1·99 + £2·76 = £9·11

---

page 39
Subtracting

1. 434 − 377 = 57
2. 521 − 466 = 55
3. 118 − 77 = 41
4. 204 − 188 = 16
5. 312 − 254 = 58
6. 723 − 686 = 37
7. 637 − 552 = 85
8. 1049 − 973 = 76
9. 202 − 16 = 186
10. 3014 − 25 = 2989
11. 5024 − 25 = 4999
12. 6006 − 18 = 5988
13. 412 − 18 = 394
14. 121 − 32 = 89
15. 2013 − 24 = 1989
16. 907 − 38 = 869
17. 486 − 239 = 247
18. 557 − 129 = 428
19. 666 − 339 = 327
20. 841 − 219 = 622
21. 755 − 549 = 206
22. 381 − 202 = 179
23. 472 − 101 = 371
24. 657 − 298 = 359
25. 646 − 554 = 92
26. 803 − 17 = 786
27. 574 − 219 = 355
28. 631 − 589 = 42
29. 7008 − 26 = 6982
30. 367 − 229 = 138
31. 304 − 268 = 36
32. 119 − 78 = 41

---

page 40
Subtracting

1. $\frac{1}{2}$ of 216 = 108 | 108 − 98 = 10 | 10 km to go
2. $\frac{1}{2}$ of 550 = 275 | 275 − 177 = 98 | 98 km to go
3. $\frac{1}{2}$ of 448 = 224 | 224 − 188 = 36 | 36 km to go
4. $\frac{1}{2}$ of 638 = 319 | 319 − 279 = 40 | 40 km to go
5. $\frac{1}{2}$ of 326 = 163 | 163 − 102 = 61 | 61 km to go
6. $\frac{1}{2}$ of 812 = 406 | 406 − 386 = 20 | 20 km to go
7. $\frac{1}{2}$ of 144 = 72 | 72 − 25 = 47 | 47 km to go

8. 214 − 178 = 36   36 go home
9. 331 − 184 − 48 = 99   99 go home
10. 277 − 102 − 73 = 102   102 go home
11. 405 − 278 − 27 = 100   100 go home
12. 245 − 166 − 41 = 38   38 go home
13. 426 − 289 − 38 = 99   99 go home
14. 371 − 203 − 52 = 116   116 go home

Number Textbook 1

Subtracting

1. $5 \times 16 = 80$	$80 - 29 - 34 + 27 = 44$	44 empty spaces
2. $5 \times 16 = 80$	$80 - 13 - 38 + 24 = 53$	53 empty spaces
3. $5 \times 16 = 80$	$80 - 31 + 19 - 23 = 45$	45 empty spaces
4. $6 \times 18 = 108$	$108 - 18 - 25 + 33 = 98$	98 empty spaces
5. $6 \times 18 = 108$	$108 - 32 - 17 + 46 = 105$	105 empty spaces
6. $6 \times 18 = 108$	$108 - 41 - 37 - 30 = 0$	0 empty spaces
7. $9 \times 22 = 198$	$198 - 19 - 51 - 76 = 52$	52 empty spaces
8. $9 \times 22 = 198$	$198 - 28 + 14 - 39 = 145$	145 empty spaces
9. $9 \times 22 = 198$	$198 - 67 - 58 + 125 = 198$	198 empty spaces

Explore

Answers will vary.

Multiples

1. multiples of 7:	7, 14, 21, 28, 35, 42, 49	14%
2. multiples of 9:	9, 18, 27, 36, 45	10%
3. multiples of 13:	13, 26, 39	6%
4. multiples of 3 and 4:	12, 24, 36, 48	8%
5. multiples of 2 and 3:	6, 12, 18, 24, 30, 36, 42, 48	16%
6. multiples of 5 and 6:	30	2%
7. multiples of 4 and 5:	20, 40	4%
8. not multiples of 2, 3, 4:	1, 5, 7, 11, 13, 17, 19, 23, 25, 29, 31, 35, 37, 41, 43, 47, 49	34%
9. multiples of 3 and 5:	15, 30, 45	6%
10. multiples of 4 and 8:	8, 16, 24, 32, 40, 48	12%

@ See above percentages.

11. 24, 18, 36, 50, 48, 16, 20
12. 24, 9, 18, 36, 48, 21
13. 24, 36, 48, 16, 20
14. 24, 18, 36, 48
15. 24, 36, 48
16. 21
17. 50, 20

Number Textbook 1

page 43
Common multiples

Properties of number **N13**

1.–10. Answers will vary.

- **1a.** 18
- **2a.** 78
- **3a.** 18
- **4a.** 60
- **5a.** 120
- **6a.** 60
- **7a.** 36
- **8a.** 36
- **9a.** 42
- **10a.** 60

11. 21 $\quad \frac{9}{21} < \frac{14}{21} \qquad \frac{3}{7} < \frac{2}{3}$

12. 20 $\quad \frac{15}{20} < \frac{16}{20} \qquad \frac{3}{4} < \frac{4}{5}$

13. 42 $\quad \frac{35}{42} > \frac{24}{42} \qquad \frac{5}{6} > \frac{4}{7}$

14. 18 $\quad \frac{48}{54} > \frac{45}{54} \qquad \frac{16}{18} > \frac{15}{18}$

15. 60 $\quad \frac{25}{60} > \frac{24}{60} \qquad \frac{5}{12} > \frac{2}{5}$

16. 50 $\quad \frac{35}{50} > \frac{22}{50} \qquad \frac{7}{10} > \frac{11}{25}$

17. 68 $\quad \frac{36}{68} < \frac{51}{68} \qquad \frac{9}{17} < \frac{3}{4}$

18. 60 $\quad \frac{35}{60} > \frac{34}{60} \qquad \frac{7}{12} > \frac{17}{30}$

page 44
Lowest common multiples

Properties of number **N13**

	2	3	4	5	6	7	8	9	10
2	2	6	4	10	6	14	8	18	10
3	6	3	12	15	6	21	24	9	30
4	4	12	4	20	12	28	8	36	20
5	10	15	20	5	30	35	40	45	10
6	6	6	12	30	6	42	24	18	30
7	14	21	28	35	42	7	56	63	70
8	8	24	8	40	24	56	8	72	40
9	18	9	36	45	18	63	72	9	90
10	10	30	20	10	30	70	40	90	10

1. 36
2. 56
3. 24

Explore

Cards	Lowest common multiple	Cards	Lowest common multiple	Cards	Lowest common multiple
2,3,5	30	3,4,7	84	4,5,8	40
2,3,7	42	3,5,6	30	4,6,7	84
2,5,6	30	3,5,7	105	4,7,8	56
2,5,7	70	3,5,8	120	5,6,7	210
2,5,8	40	3,6,7	42	5,6,8	120
2,6,7	42	3,7,8	168	5,7,8	280
2,7,8	56	4,5,6	60	6,7,8	168
3,4,5	60	4,5,7	140		

23 sets altogether.

Number Textbook 1

Divisibility

1. no	**2.** yes	**3.** no	**4.** yes	**5.** yes
6. yes	**7.** yes	**8.** no	**9.** yes	**10.** yes
11. no	**12.** no			

℮

1. $34 \div 25 = 1 \text{ r } 9$ 1 box can be filled, 9 flowers left over.
2. $48 \div 25 = 1 \text{ r } 23$ 1 box can be filled, 23 flowers left over.
3. $66 \div 25 = 2 \text{ r } 16$ 2 boxes can be filled, 16 flowers left over.
4. $84 \div 25 = 3 \text{ r } 9$ 3 boxes can be filled, 9 flowers left over.
5. $132 \div 25 = 5 \text{ r } 7$ 5 boxes can be filled, 7 flowers left over.
6. $116 \div 25 = 4 \text{ r } 16$ 4 boxes can be filled, 16 flowers left over.
7. $224 \div 25 = 8 \text{ r } 24$ 8 boxes can be filled, 24 flowers left over.
8. $314 \div 25 = 12 \text{ r } 14$ 12 boxes can be filled, 14 flowers left over.
9. $152 \div 25 = 6 \text{ r } 2$ 6 boxes can be filled, 2 flowers left over.
10. $168 \div 25 = 6 \text{ r } 18$ 6 boxes can be filled, 18 flowers left over.
11. $322 \div 25 = 12 \text{ r } 22$ 12 boxes can be filled, 22 flowers left over.
12. $98 \div 25 = 3 \text{ r } 23$ 3 boxes can be filled, 23 flowers left over.

13. 86 divides by 2
14. 420 divides by 2, 4
15. 214 divides by 2
16. 152 divides by 2, 4, 8
17. 78 divides by 2
18. 108 divides by 2, 4
19. 92 divides by 2, 4
20. 146 divides by 2
21. 262 divides by 2
22. 188 divides by 2, 4
23. 324 divides by 2, 4
24. 504 divides by 2, 4, 8

Divisibility

1. 462   divides by 3   **1a.** divides by 6   ℮ does not divide by 9
2. 558   divides by 3   **2a.** divides by 6   ℮ divides by 9
3. 662   does not divide by 3   **3a.** does not divide by 6
    ℮ does not divide by 9
4. 435   divides by 3   **4a.** does not divide by 6   ℮ does not divide by 9
5. 1008   divides by 3   **5a.** divides by 6   ℮ divides by 9
6. 990   divides by 3   **6a.** divides by 6   ℮ divides by 9
7. 738   divides by 3   **7a.** divides by 6   ℮ divides by 9
8. 444   divides by 3   **8a.** divides by 6   ℮ does not divide by 9
9. 6021   divides by 3   **9a.** does not divide by 6   ℮ divides by 9
10. 7398   divides by 3   **10a.** divides by 6   ℮ divides by 9
11. 9045   divides by 3   **11a.** does not divide by 6   ℮ divides by 9

page 46 cont ...

12. no	13. no	14. yes	15. yes
16. yes	17. no	18. no	19. yes
12a. no	13a. no	14a. yes	15a. yes
16a. yes	17a. no	18a. no	19a. yes

℮

14. 360	60 teams of 6	40 teams of 9
15. 144	24 teams of 6	16 teams of 9
16. 450	75 teams of 6	50 teams of 9
17. 252	42 teams of 6	28 teams of 9

page 47
Divisibility

·	÷ 2	÷ 3	÷ 4	÷ 5	÷ 6	÷ 8	÷ 9	÷ 10	÷ 25
60	✓	✓	✓	✓	✓			✓	
720	✓	✓	✓	✓	✓	✓	✓	✓	
945		✓		✓		✓	✓		
7644	✓	✓	✓		✓				
1000	✓		✓	✓		✓		✓	✓
2508	✓	✓	✓		✓				
1462	✓								

1. 84	2. 56	3. 63

Explore

245, 364, 259 divisible by 7
Test for divisibility by 14: first halve the number, then use the test for divisibility by 7. Numbers divisible by 14 must also be even.

page 48
Multiplying decimals

1. 10×3.8 m = 38 m	2. 10×4.4 m = 44 m	3. 10×1.5 m = 15 m
4. 10×3.5 m = 35 m	5. 10×1.2 m = 12 m	6. 10×2.8 m = 28 m
7. 10×3.1 m = 31 m	8. 10×0.9 m = 9 m	9. 10×0.7 m = 7 m
10. 10×4.1 m = 41 m	11. 10×2.1 m = 21 m	12. 10×3.7 m = 37 m

Number Textbook 1

page 48 cont ...

13. $10 \times 2 \cdot 7 = 27$ **14.** $10 \times 1 \cdot 3 = 13$ **15.** $10 \times 9 \cdot 5 = 95$
16. $0 \cdot 8 \times 10 = 8$ **17.** $10 \times 3 \cdot 4 = 34$ **18.** $10 \times 13 \cdot 4 = 134$
19. $10 \times 21 \cdot 3 = 213$ **20.** $6 \times 10 = 60$ **21.** $10 \times 19 \cdot 7 = 197$
22. $10 \times 43 \cdot 8 = 438$ **23.** $10 \times 4 = 40$ **24.** $10 \times 12 \cdot 5 = 125$
25. $10 \times 61 \cdot 4 = 614$

---

page 49   Place-value **N15**
Multiplying decimals

1. $10 \times 1 \cdot 74 = 17 \cdot 4$ **2.** $10 \times 2 \cdot 31 = 23 \cdot 1$ **3.** $100 \times 1 \cdot 86 = 186$
4. $10 \times 1 \cdot 92 = 19 \cdot 2$ **5.** $100 \times 3 \cdot 16 = 316$ **6.** $10 \times 2 \cdot 73 = 27 \cdot 3$
7. $100 \times 0 \cdot 93 = 93$ **8.** $10 \times 0 \cdot 76 = 7 \cdot 6$ **9.** $100 \times 4 \cdot 7 = 470$
10. $100 \times 2 \cdot 09 = 209$

11. $10 \times £3 \cdot 26 = £32 \cdot 60$ **12.** $10 \times £5 \cdot 93 = £59 \cdot 30$
13. $10 \times £9 \cdot 34 = £93 \cdot 40$ **14.** $10 \times £1 \cdot 75 = £17 \cdot 50$
15. $10 \times £6 \cdot 84 = £68 \cdot 40$ **16.** $10 \times £11 \cdot 20 = £112 \cdot 00$
17. $10 \times £4 \cdot 82 = £48 \cdot 20$ **18.** $10 \times £7 \cdot 02 = £70 \cdot 20$
19. $10 \times £21 \cdot 30 = £213 \cdot 00$ **20.** $10 \times £14 \cdot 51 = £145 \cdot 10$
21. $10 \times £7 \cdot 39 = £73 \cdot 90$ **22.** $10 \times £0 \cdot 28 = £2 \cdot 80$

11a. $100 \times £3 \cdot 26 = £326 \cdot 00$ **12a.** $100 \times £5 \cdot 93 = £593 \cdot 00$
13a. $100 \times £9 \cdot 34 = £934 \cdot 00$ **14a.** $100 \times £1 \cdot 75 = £175 \cdot 00$
15a. $100 \times £6 \cdot 84 = £684 \cdot 00$ **16a.** $100 \times £11 \cdot 20 = £1120 \cdot 00$
17a. $100 \times £4 \cdot 82 = £482 \cdot 00$ **18a.** $100 \times £7 \cdot 02 = £702 \cdot 00$
19a. $100 \times £21 \cdot 30 = £2130 \cdot 00$ **20a.** $100 \times £14 \cdot 51 = £1451 \cdot 00$
21a. $100 \times £7 \cdot 39 = £739 \cdot 00$ **22a.** $100 \times £0 \cdot 28 = £28 \cdot 00$

---

page 50   Place-value **N15**
Multiplying decimals

1. $100 \times 2 \cdot 3 = 230$ **2.** $10 \times 1 \cdot 5 = 15$ **3.** $10 \times 3 \cdot 4 = 34$
4. $100 \times 7 \cdot 6 = 760$ **5.** $100 \times 4 \cdot 8 = 480$ **6.** $10 \times 31 \cdot 2 = 312$
7. $100 \times 4 \cdot 23 = 423$ **8.** $100 \times 6 \cdot 75 = 675$ **9.** $10 \times 8 \cdot 09 = 80 \cdot 9$
10. $100 \times 9 \cdot 38 = 938$ **11.** $100 \times 16 \cdot 45 = 1645$ **12.** $10 \times 9 \cdot 38 = 93 \cdot 8$
13. $100 \times 8 \cdot 95 = 895$ **14.** $100 \times 67 = 6700$ **15.** $1000 \times 0 \cdot 73 = 730$
16. $1000 \times 0 \cdot 21 = 210$

17. Stephen cycles $3 \cdot 7$ km $\times 10 = 37$ km/week, 37 km $\times 2 = 74$ km in a
fortnight, 37 km $\times 20 = 740$ km in 20 weeks, 37 km $\times 48 = 1776$ km in
1 year.

Number Textbook 1

18. Day 1   3 mm × 10 = 30 mm = 3 cm
    Day 2   3 cm × 10 = 30 cm
    Day 3   30 cm × 10 = 300 cm = 3 m
    Day 4   3 m × 10 = 30 m
    Day 5   30 m × 10 = 300 m
    Day 6   300 m × 10 = 3000 m = 3 km
    After 6 days the beanstalk will be 3 km high.

Explore

	× 10	× 100	× 1000	× 20	× 200
2·1	21	210	2100	42	420

× 10   move decimal point 1 place right
× 100   move decimal point 2 places right
× 1000   move decimal point 3 places right
× 20   double and then × 10
× 200   double and then × 100

---

page 51
Dividing decimals

Place-value **N16**

1. 47·3 km ÷ 10 = 4·73 km
2. 61·4 km ÷ 10 = 6·14 km
3. 9·8 km ÷ 10 = 0·98 km
4. 11 km ÷ 10 = 1·1 km
5. 3·5 km ÷ 10 = 0·35 km
6. 16·3 km ÷ 10 = 1·63 km
7. 75 km ÷ 10 = 7·5 km
8. 8 km ÷ 10 = 0·8 km
9. 119·5 km ÷ 10 = 11·95 km

@

1. 47·3 km × 20 = 946 km
2. 61·4 km × 20 = 1228 km
3. 9·8 km × 20 = 196 km
4. 11 km × 20 = 220 km
5. 3·5 km × 20 = 70 km
6. 16·3 km × 20 = 326 km
7. 75 km × 20 = 1500 km
8. 8 km × 20 = 160 km
9. 119·5 km × 20 = 2390 km

10. 14 ÷ 10 = 1·4
11. 1·73 ÷ 10 = 0·173
12. 6 ÷ 10 = 0·6
13. 8·7 ÷ 10 = 0·87
14. 73 ÷ 10 = 7·3
15. 7·0 ÷ 10 = 0·7
16. 9·75 ÷ 10 = 0·975
17. 0·3 ÷ 10 = 0·03
18. 17·6 ÷ 10 = 1·76
19. 1·1 ÷ 10 = 0·11

Number Textbook 1

Dividing decimals

1. 45·6 cm ÷ 100 = 0·456 m
2. 28·5 cm ÷ 100 = 0·285 m
3. 140·6 cm ÷ 100 = 1·406 m
4. 9·6 cm ÷ 100 = 0·096 m
5. 230 cm ÷ 100 = 2·3 m
6. 8·7 cm ÷ 100 = 0·087 m
7. 51·6 cm ÷ 100 = 0·516 m
8. 60·5 cm ÷ 100 = 0·605 m
9. 98 cm ÷ 100 = 0·98 m
10. 121 cm ÷ 100 = 1·21 m

11. 36 ÷ 100 = 0·36
12. 72·5 ÷ 100 = 0·725
13. 59 ÷ 100 = 0·59
14. 40·3 ÷ 100 = 0·403
15. 146 ÷ 100 = 1·46
16. 4·6 ÷ 100 = 0·046
17. 7 ÷ 100 = 0·07
18. 0·8 ÷ 100 = 0·008
19. 7·7 ÷ 100 = 0·077
20. 96 ÷ 100 = 0·96

Dividing decimals

1. 3·8 ÷ 10 = 0·38
2. 76·2 ÷ 100 = 0·762
3. 0·6 ÷ 10 = 0·06
4. 0·04 ÷ 100 = 0·0004
5. 9·1 ÷ 10 = 0·91
6. 45·62 ÷ 10 = 4·562
7. 0·8 ÷ 100 = 0·008
8. 7·5 ÷ 100 = 0·075
9. 96·3 ÷ 10 = 9·63
10. 1·25 ÷ 100 = 0·0125
11. 77·3 ÷ 100 = 0·773

12. 8·3 kg ÷ 100 = 0·083 kg = 83 g   Each ball weighs 83 g.
13. £75·30 ÷ 10 = £7·53   Each winner gets £7·53.
    £10 − £7·53 = £2·47   They each need £2·47 more to have £10.
14. 100 m ÷ 10 m = 10   9·92 sec ÷ 10 = 0·992 sec for 10 m
15. 0·72 m ÷ 10 = 0·072 m = 7·2 cm   Each brick is 7·2 cm long.
    7·2 cm × 14 = 1·008 m   14 bricks are needed.

Multiplying

1. 45p × 7 = 315p   £3·15
2. 45p × 9 = 405p   £4·05
3. 45p × 6 = 270p   £2·70
4. 39p × 9 = 351p   £3·51
5. 39p × 7 = 273p   £2·73
6. 39p × 8 = 312p   £3·12
7. 47p × 8 = 376p   £3·76
8. 47p × 5 = 235p   £2·35
9. 47p × 6 = 282p   £2·82

10. 4 × 73 = 292
11. 3 × 42 = 126
12. 5 × 35 = 175
13. 7 × 61 = 427
14. 8 × 33 = 264
15. 6 × 18 = 108
16. 9 × 75 = 675
17. 4 × 83 = 332
18. 7 × 29 = 203
19. 8 × 46 = 368

Number Textbook 1

Multiplying

1. £317 × 2 = £634
2. £463 × 2 = £926
3. £542 × 3 = £1626
4. £160 × 4 = £640
5. £285 × 6 = £1710
6. £125 × 8 = £1000
7. £665 × 2 = £1330
8. £217 × 3 = £651
9. £85 × 5 = £425
10. £730 × 3 = £2190

@ 1, 2, and 7, no discount

3. £1626 − £162·60 = £1463·40
4. £640 − £64 = £576
5. £1710 − £171 = £1539
6. £1000 − £100 = £900
8. £651 − £65·10 = £585·90
9. £425 − £42·50 = £382·50
10. £2190 − £219 = £1971

11. 3 × 46 = 138
12. 4 × 22 = 88
13. 305 = 5 × 61
14. 4 × 53 = 212
15. 168 = 6 × 28

Explore

11 × 9 = 99   22 × 9 = 198   33 × 9 = 297
44 × 9 = 396   55 × 9 = 495   66 × 9 = 594
77 × 9 = 693   88 × 9 = 792   99 × 9 = 891

The tens digit is always 9. The units and hundreds digit total 9. The hundreds digit of the answer is 1 less than the tens digit of the chosen number.

11 × 8 = 88   22 × 8 = 176   33 × 8 = 264
44 × 8 = 352   55 × 8 = 440   66 × 8 = 528
77 × 8 = 616   88 × 8 = 704   99 × 8 = 792

The hundreds digit of the answer is 1 less than the tens digit of the chosen number (up to 88). The tens digits decrease by 1 (except from 55 × 8 to 66 × 8). The units digits decrease by 2.

Multiplying

A 3 × 197 = 591
C 4 × 158 = 632
E 5 × 126 = 630
B 8 × 76 = 608
D 9 × 65 = 585
F 7 × 83 = 581
G 6 × 95 = 570
H 3 × 172 = 516

In descending order: C, E, B, A, D, F, G, H

1. (£84 × 3) + (£42 × 4) = £252 + £168 = £420   £500 − £420 = £80
   There will be £80 change.
2. 52 × 7 = 364   Karen has been swimming 364 times.

Number Textbook 1

3. 365 days × 4 = 1460 days   There is 1 leap year in 4 years.
   1460 + 1 = 1461 days
   1510 − 1461 = 49 days   49 ÷ 7 = 7   There are 7 weeks until Tanya is
   1510 days old.
4. £147 × 6 = £882   £93 × 9 = £837   Paying £93 over 9 months is cheaper.
   £882 − £837 = £45   It is £45 cheaper.

---

page 57   Multiplication/division   **N18**
Multiplying by 1–digit numbers

1. £436 × 8 = £3488   2. £189 × 9 = £1701   3. £328 × 6 = £1968
4. £308 × 5 = £1540   5. £543 × 4 = £2172   6. £136 × 7 = £952
7. £247 × 9 = £2223   8. £198 × 8 = £1584

9. 7 × 362 = 2534   10. 8 × 385 = 3080   11. 4 × 319 = 1276
12. 516 × 4 = 2064   13. 9 × 187 = 1683   14. 763 × 7 = 5341
15. 3 × 343 = 1029

In ascending order: 1029, 1276, 1683, 2064, 2534, 3080, 5341

---

page 58   Multiplication/division   **N18**
Multiplying by 1–digit numbers

1. 3521 × 7 = 24 647   correct   2. 4328 × 5 = 21 640   correct
3. 9546 × 3 = 28 638   correct   4. 5314 × 4 = 21 256   correct

5. 2789 × 5 = 13 945   incorrect   6. 7162 × 6 = 42 972   incorrect
7. 1958 × 8 = 15 664   incorrect   8. 4629 × 4 = 18 516   incorrect
9. 6542 × 7 = 45 794   incorrect

@   1. 24 647 − 20 000 = 4647   2. 21 640 − 20 000 = 1640
    3. 28 638 − 20 000 = 8638   4. 21 256 − 20 000 = 1256
    5. 20 000 − 13 945 = 6055   6. 42 972 − 20 000 = 22 972
    7. 20 000 − 15 664 = 4336   8. 20 000 − 18 516 = 1484
    9. 45 794 − 20 000 = 25 794

10. 4 × 3176 = 12 704   11. 5 × 4826 = 24 130   12. 4713 × 9 = 42 417
13. 6 × 4849 = 29 094   14. 7 × 8320 = 58 240   15. 5 × 4065 = 20 325
16. 3906 × 4 = 15 624

Number Textbook 1

Multiplying by 2–digit numbers

1.	$217 \times 34 = 7378$	7378 cm^2	2.	$286 \times 35 = 10\ 010$	$10\ 010 \text{ cm}^2$
3.	$209 \times 41 = 8569$	8569 cm^2	4.	$109 \times 45 = 4905$	4905 cm^2
5.	$316 \times 63 = 19\ 908$	$19\ 908 \text{ cm}^2$	6.	$196 \times 54 = 10\ 584$	$10\ 584 \text{ cm}^2$
7.	$223 \times 48 = 10\ 704$	$10\ 704 \text{ cm}^2$	8.	$146 \times 34 = 4964$	4964 cm^2
9.	$243 \times 68 = 16\ 524$	$16\ 524 \text{ cm}^2$			

Explore

Largest possible answer: $542 \times 63 = 34\ 146$
Smallest possible answer: $356 \times 24 = 8544$

Multiplying and dividing

1.	$5 \times 17 = 85$	$85 \div 5 = 17$	$85 \div 17 = 5$
2.	$4 \times 3 \cdot 2 = 12 \cdot 8$	$12 \cdot 8 \div 4 = 3 \cdot 2$	$12 \cdot 8 \div 3 \cdot 2 = 4$
3.	$6 \times 75 = 450$	$450 \div 75 = 6$	$450 \div 6 = 75$
4.	$2 \cdot 8 \times 5 = 14$	$14 \div 5 = 2 \cdot 8$	$14 \div 2 \cdot 8 = 5$
5.	$20 \times 0 \cdot 3 = 6$	$6 \div 0 \cdot 3 = 20$	$6 \div 20 = 0 \cdot 3$
6.	$25 \times 14 = 350$	$350 \div 14 = 25$	$350 \div 25 = 14$
7.	$32 \times 19 = 608$	$608 \div 19 = 32$	$608 \div 32 = 19$
8.	$4 \cdot 7 \times 30 = 141$	$141 \div 30 = 4 \cdot 7$	$141 \div 4 \cdot 7 = 30$

9.	350, 7, 50			
9a.	$7 \times 50 = 350$	$50 \times 7 = 350$	$350 \div 7 = 50$	$350 \div 50 = 7$
10.	120, 4, 30			
10a.	$4 \times 30 = 120$	$30 \times 4 = 120$	$120 \div 4 = 30$	$120 \div 30 = 4$
11.	240, 40, 6			
11a.	$40 \times 6 = 240$	$6 \times 40 = 240$	$240 \div 6 = 40$	$240 \div 40 = 6$
12.	140, 7, 20			
12a.	$7 \times 20 = 140$	$20 \times 7 = 140$	$140 \div 7 = 20$	$140 \div 20 = 7$
13.	240, 8, 30			
13a.	$8 \times 30 = 240$	$30 \times 8 = 240$	$240 \div 8 = 30$	$240 \div 30 = 8$
14.	350, 70, 5			
14a.	$70 \times 5 = 350$	$5 \times 70 = 350$	$350 \div 5 = 70$	$350 \div 70 = 5$
15.	100, 25, 4			
15a.	$4 \times 25 = 100$	$25 \times 4 = 100$	$100 \div 4 = 25$	$100 \div 25 = 4$
16.	175, 7, 25			
16a.	$7 \times 25 = 175$	$25 \times 7 = 175$	$175 \div 7 = 25$	$175 \div 25 = 7$
17.	225, 9, 25			
17a.	$9 \times 25 = 225$	$25 \times 9 = 225$	$225 \div 9 = 25$	$225 \div 25 = 9$

Number Textbook 1

page 61

Multiplication/division **N19**

Multiplying and dividing

1. $\frac{1}{3}$ of 2·7 = 0·9	**2.** 0·4 × 3 = 1·2	**3.** 1·8 × 2 = 3·6
4. 2·7 ÷ 0·9 = 3	**5.** 2·7 ÷ 0·9 = 3	**6.** $\frac{1}{4}$ of 3·6 = 0·9
7. 1·2 × 3 = 3·6	**8.** 4·8 ÷ 4 = 1·2	**9.** 12 ÷ 0·4 = 30
10. $\frac{1}{2}$ of 1·8 = 0·9	**11.** 4 × 0·9 = 3·6	**12.** 3·6 ÷ 1·2 = 3

13. 2·4, 4, 0·6 **14.** 1, 5, 0·2 **15.** 4, 8, 0·5 **16.** 2, 5, 0·4

13. 2·4 ÷ 4 = 0·6 2·4 ÷ 0·6 = 4	**14.** 1 ÷ 5 = 0·2 1 ÷ 0·2 = 5	**15.** 4 ÷ 8 = 0·5 4 ÷ 0·5 = 8	**16.** 2 ÷ 0·4 = 5 2 ÷ 5 = 0·4

---

page 62

Multiplication/division **N19**

Multiplying and dividing

1. £84 × 5 = £420 £420 – £350 = £70 Dad needs £70 more.
2. 33 cm ÷ 15 = 2·2 cm 2·2 cm × 6 = 13·2 cm
   6 game boxes take up 13·2 cm
3. 12 × 16 = 192 200 – 192 = 8 There are 8 months
   until Sammy has been alive for 200 months.
4. 57 g ÷ 6 = 9·5 g 9·5 g × 10 = 95 g 10 marbles weigh 95 g.
5. 96 l ÷ 3·2 l = 30 30 buckets are needed.
6. 7 days × 57 = 399 days The trip took 399 days.

Explore

2 × 0·6 = 1·2	1·2 ÷ 2 = 0·6	1·2 ÷ 0·6 = 2
3 × 0·4 = 1·2	1·2 ÷ 3 = 0·4	1·2 ÷ 0·4 = 0·3
3 × 0·6 = 1·8	1·8 ÷ 3 = 0·6	1·8 ÷ 0·6 = 3
5 × 0·4 = 2	2 ÷ 5 = 0·4	2 ÷ 0·4 = 5
5 × 0·6 = 3	3 ÷ 5 = 0·6	3 ÷ 0·6 = 5

---

page 63

Multiplication/division **N20**

Remainders

1. 43 ÷ 6 = 7$\frac{1}{6}$	**2.** 29 ÷ 4 = 7$\frac{1}{4}$	**3.** 31 ÷ 2 = 15$\frac{1}{2}$
4. 43 ÷ 5 = 8$\frac{3}{5}$	**5.** 73 ÷ 7 = 10$\frac{3}{7}$	**6.** 29 ÷ 3 = 9$\frac{2}{3}$
7. 64 ÷ 9 = 7$\frac{1}{9}$	**8.** 51 ÷ 6 = 8$\frac{1}{2}$	**9.** 33 ÷ 8 = 4$\frac{1}{8}$
10. 86 ÷ 9 = 9$\frac{5}{9}$		

Number Textbook 1

11. $41 \div 3 = 13\frac{2}{3}$ 14 packs needed   12. $75 \div 4 = 18\frac{3}{4}$ 19 packs needed

13. $47 \div 3 = 15\frac{2}{3}$ 16 packs needed   14. $81 \div 6 = 13\frac{1}{2}$ 14 packs needed

15. $76 \div 5 = 15\frac{1}{5}$ 16 packs needed   16. $86 \div 7 = 12\frac{2}{7}$ 13 packs needed

17. $51 \div 4 = 12\frac{3}{4}$ 13 packs needed   18. $75 \div 6 = 12\frac{1}{2}$ 13 packs needed

19. $87 \div 9 = 9\frac{2}{3}$ 10 packs needed   20. $93 \div 8 = 11\frac{5}{8}$ 12 packs needed

---

page 64
Remainders

1. $73 \div 10 = 7\frac{3}{10} = 7.3$ 7 full trays   2. $19 \div 10 = 1\frac{9}{10} = 1.9$ 1 full tray

3. $29 \div 10 = 2\frac{9}{10} = 2.9$ 2 full trays   4. $87 \div 10 = 8\frac{7}{10} = 8.7$ 8 full trays

5. $93 \div 10 = 9\frac{3}{10} = 9.3$ 9 full trays   6. $111 \div 10 = 11\frac{1}{10} = 11.1$ 11 full trays

7. $67 \div 10 = 6\frac{7}{10} = 6.7$ 6 full trays

8. $42 \div 10 = 4\frac{2}{10} = 4\frac{1}{5} = 4.2$ 4 full trays

9. $147 \div 100 = 1\frac{47}{100} = 1.47$ 2 bags   10. $359 \div 100 = 3\frac{59}{100} = 3.59$ 4 bags

11. $731 \div 100 = 7\frac{31}{100} = 7.31$ 8 bags   12. $867 \div 100 = 8\frac{67}{100} = 8.67$ 9 bags

13. $478 \div 100 = 4\frac{78}{100} = 4.78$ 5 bags   14. $209 \div 100 = 2\frac{9}{100} = 2.09$ 3 bags

15. $142 \div 100 = 1\frac{42}{100} (= 1\frac{21}{50}) = 1.42$ 2 bags

16. $790 \div 100 = 7\frac{90}{100} (= 7\frac{9}{10}) = 7.90$ 8 bags

17. $703 \div 100 = 7\frac{3}{100} = 7.03$ 8 bags

18. $84 \div 100 = \frac{84}{100} (= \frac{21}{25}) = 0.84$ 1 bag

19. $70 \div 100 = \frac{70}{100} (= \frac{7}{10}) = 0.70$ 1 bag

20. $1042 \div 100 = 10\frac{42}{100} (= 10\frac{21}{50}) = 10.42$ 11 bags

21. $1369 \div 100 = 13\frac{69}{100} = 13.69$ 14 bags

22. $2718 \div 100 = 27\frac{18}{100} (= 27\frac{9}{50}) = 27.18$ 28 bags

23. $9764 \div 100 = 97\frac{64}{100} (= 97\frac{16}{25}) = 97.64$ 98 bags

---

page 65
Remainders

1. $31\,l \div 5 = 6\frac{1}{5}\,l = 6.2\,l$ 2. $43\,l \div 5 = 8\frac{3}{5}\,l = 8.6\,l$

3. $76\,l \div 5 = 15\frac{1}{5}\,l = 15.2\,l$ 4. $89\,l \div 5 = 17\frac{4}{5}\,l = 17.8\,l$

Number Textbook 1

5. $38\,l \div 5 = 7\frac{3}{5}\,l = 7.6\,l$

6. $47\,l \div 5 = 9\frac{2}{5}\,l = 9.4\,l$

7. $29\,l \div 5 = 5\frac{4}{5}\,l = 5.8\,l$

8. $36\,l \div 5 = 7\frac{1}{5}\,l = 7.2\,l$

9. $47 \div 10 = 4.7$ $23 \div 5 = 4.6$ $\frac{1}{10}$ of 47 larger

10. $35 \div 4 = 8.75$ $860 \div 100 = 8.6$ $\frac{1}{4}$ of 35 larger

11. $13 \div 2 = 6.5$ $32 \div 5 = 6.4$ $\frac{1}{2}$ of 13 larger

12. $70 \div 4 = 17.5$ $176 \div 10 = 17.6$ $\frac{1}{10}$ of 176 larger

13. $94 \div 100 = 0.94$ $19 \div 2 = 9.5$ $\frac{1}{2}$ of 19 larger

14. $(50 \div 5) \times 2 = 20$ $90 \div 4 = 22.5$ $\frac{1}{4}$ of 90 larger

15. $(61 \div 10) \times 3 = 18.3$ $76 \div 2 = 38$ $\frac{1}{2}$ of 76 larger

16. $(42 \div 5) \times 3 = 25.2$ $(55 \div 10) \times 7 = 38.5$ $\frac{7}{10}$ of 55 larger

17. $70 \div 8 = 8\frac{6}{8} = 8\frac{3}{4}$ The minibus needs to make 9 trips.

18. Jake could buy pizzas in these combinations:

    $£4 \times 5 = £20$ 5 large, no change

    $(£3 \times 1) + (£4 \times 4) = £19$ 1 small, 4 large, £1 change

    $(£3 \times 2) + (£4 \times 3) = £18$ 2 small, 3 large, £2 change

    $(£3 \times 3) + (£4 \times 2) = £17$ 3 small, 2 large, £3 change

    $(£3 \times 4) + (£4 \times 2) = £20$ 4 small, 2 large, no change

    $(£3 \times 5) + (£4 \times 1) = £19$ 5 small, 1 large, £1 change

    $£3 \times 6 = £18$ 6 small, £2 change

Mixed numbers and improper fractions

1. $2\frac{3}{8} = \frac{19}{8}$ 19 slices

2. $2\frac{5}{6} = \frac{17}{6}$ 17 slices

3. $1\frac{7}{8} = \frac{15}{8}$ 15 slices

4. $3\frac{1}{4} = \frac{13}{4}$ 13 slices

5. $2\frac{2}{3} = \frac{8}{3}$ 8 slices

6. $1\frac{1}{6} = \frac{7}{6}$ 7 slices

7. $2\frac{2}{7} = \frac{16}{7}$ 16 slices

8. $1\frac{7}{9} = \frac{16}{9}$ 16 slices

9. $2\frac{11}{12} = \frac{35}{12}$ 35 slices

10. $1\frac{7}{10} = \frac{17}{10}$ 17 slices

11. $3\frac{4}{5} = \frac{19}{5}$

12. $1\frac{2}{5} = \frac{7}{5}$

13. $2\frac{3}{5} = \frac{13}{5}$

14. $3\frac{1}{5} = \frac{16}{5}$

15. $2\frac{4}{5} = \frac{14}{5}$

16. $3\frac{3}{5} = \frac{18}{5}$

17. $6\frac{1}{5} = \frac{31}{5}$

18. $1\frac{4}{5} = \frac{9}{5}$

19. $2\frac{2}{5} = \frac{12}{5}$

20. $4\frac{2}{5} = \frac{22}{5}$

Mixed numbers and improper fractions

1. $\frac{17}{8} = 2\frac{1}{8}$ trays

2. $\frac{23}{10} = 2\frac{3}{10}$ trays

3. $\frac{16}{6} = 2\frac{4}{6} = 2\frac{2}{3}$ trays

4. $\frac{29}{4} = 7\frac{1}{4}$ trays

5. $\frac{20}{8} = 2\frac{4}{8} = 2\frac{1}{2}$ trays

6. $\frac{13}{5} = 2\frac{3}{5}$ trays

7. $\frac{20}{3} = 6\frac{2}{3}$ trays

8. $\frac{40}{6} = 6\frac{4}{6} = 6\frac{2}{3}$ trays

9. $\frac{42}{10} = 4\frac{2}{10} = 4\frac{1}{5}$ trays

ⓔ 1. $7\frac{7}{8}$ 2. $7\frac{7}{10}$ 3. $7\frac{1}{3}$ 4. $2\frac{3}{4}$ 5. $7\frac{1}{2}$

6. $7\frac{2}{5}$ 7. $3\frac{1}{3}$ 8. $3\frac{1}{3}$ 9. $5\frac{4}{5}$

Explore

There are 56 mixed numbers between 2 and 4 that can be made:

$2\frac{1}{3} = \frac{7}{3}, 2\frac{1}{4} = \frac{9}{4}, 2\frac{1}{5} = \frac{11}{5}, 2\frac{1}{6} = \frac{13}{6}, 2\frac{1}{7} = \frac{15}{7}, 2\frac{1}{8} = \frac{17}{8}, 2\frac{1}{9} = \frac{19}{9}$

$2\frac{3}{4} = \frac{11}{4}, 2\frac{3}{5} = \frac{13}{5}, 2\frac{3}{6} = \frac{15}{6}, 2\frac{3}{7} = \frac{17}{7}, 2\frac{3}{8} = \frac{19}{8}, 2\frac{3}{9} = \frac{21}{9}$

$2\frac{4}{5} = \frac{14}{5}, 2\frac{4}{6} = \frac{16}{6}, 2\frac{4}{7} = \frac{18}{7}, 2\frac{4}{8} = \frac{20}{8}, 2\frac{4}{9} = \frac{22}{9}$

$2\frac{5}{6} = \frac{17}{6}, 2\frac{5}{7} = \frac{19}{7}, 2\frac{5}{8} = \frac{21}{8}, 2\frac{5}{9} = \frac{23}{9}$

$2\frac{6}{7} = \frac{20}{7}, 2\frac{6}{8} = \frac{22}{8}, 2\frac{6}{9} = \frac{24}{9}$

$2\frac{7}{8} = \frac{23}{8}, 2\frac{7}{9} = \frac{25}{9}$

$2\frac{8}{9} = \frac{26}{9}$

$3\frac{1}{2} = \frac{7}{2}, 3\frac{1}{4} = \frac{13}{4}, 3\frac{1}{5} = \frac{16}{5}, 3\frac{1}{6} = \frac{19}{6}, 3\frac{1}{7} = \frac{22}{7}, 3\frac{1}{8} = \frac{25}{8}, 3\frac{1}{9} = \frac{28}{9}$

$3\frac{2}{4} = \frac{14}{4}, 3\frac{2}{5} = \frac{17}{5}, 3\frac{2}{6} = \frac{20}{6}, 3\frac{2}{7} = \frac{23}{7}, 3\frac{2}{8} = \frac{26}{8}, 3\frac{2}{9} = \frac{29}{9}$

$3\frac{4}{5} = \frac{19}{5}, 3\frac{4}{6} = \frac{22}{6}, 3\frac{4}{7} = \frac{25}{7}, 3\frac{4}{8} = \frac{28}{8}, 3\frac{4}{9} = \frac{31}{9}$

$3\frac{5}{6} = \frac{23}{6}, 3\frac{5}{7} = \frac{26}{7}, 3\frac{5}{8} = \frac{29}{8}, 3\frac{5}{9} = \frac{32}{9}$

$3\frac{6}{7} = \frac{27}{7}, 3\frac{6}{8} = \frac{30}{8}, 3\frac{6}{9} = \frac{33}{9}$

$3\frac{7}{8} = \frac{31}{8}, 3\frac{7}{9} = \frac{34}{9}$

$3\frac{8}{9} = \frac{35}{9}$

Fractions in order:

$2\frac{1}{9}, 2\frac{1}{8}, 2\frac{1}{7}, 2\frac{1}{6}, 2\frac{1}{5}, 2\frac{1}{4}, 2\frac{1}{3} = 2\frac{3}{9}, 2\frac{3}{8}, 2\frac{3}{7}, 2\frac{4}{9}, 2\frac{3}{6} = 2\frac{4}{8}, 2\frac{5}{9}, 2\frac{4}{7}, 2\frac{3}{5}, 2\frac{5}{8},$

$2\frac{4}{6} = 2\frac{6}{9}, 2\frac{5}{7}, 2\frac{3}{4} = 2\frac{6}{8}, 2\frac{7}{9}, 2\frac{4}{5}, 2\frac{5}{6}, 2\frac{6}{7}, 2\frac{7}{8}, 2\frac{8}{9}, 3\frac{1}{9}, 3\frac{1}{8}, 3\frac{1}{7}, 3\frac{1}{6}, 3\frac{1}{5}, 3\frac{2}{9},$

$3\frac{1}{4} = 3\frac{2}{8}, 3\frac{2}{7}, 3\frac{2}{6}, 3\frac{2}{5}, 3\frac{4}{9}, 3\frac{1}{2} = 3\frac{2}{4} = 3\frac{4}{8}, 3\frac{5}{9}, 3\frac{4}{7}, 3\frac{5}{8}, 3\frac{4}{6} = 3\frac{6}{9}, 3\frac{5}{7}, 3\frac{6}{8},$

$3\frac{7}{9}, 3\frac{4}{5}, 3\frac{5}{6}, 3\frac{6}{7}, 3\frac{7}{8}, 3\frac{8}{9}$

Number Textbook 1

Mixed numbers and improper fractions

1. $2\frac{1}{4} = \frac{9}{4}$ 2. $2\frac{4}{7} = \frac{18}{7}$ 3. $3\frac{2}{9} = \frac{29}{9}$ 4. $3\frac{2}{5} = \frac{17}{5}$

5. $3\frac{6}{11} = \frac{39}{11}$ 6. $4\frac{1}{2} = \frac{9}{2}$ 7. $3\frac{3}{4} = \frac{15}{4} = \frac{30}{8}$ 8. $1\frac{4}{5} = \frac{9}{5} = \frac{18}{10}$

9. $4\frac{2}{3} = \frac{14}{3} = \frac{28}{6}$ 10. $1\frac{5}{7} = \frac{12}{7} = \frac{24}{14}$ 11. $2\frac{1}{6} = \frac{13}{6} = \frac{26}{12}$ 12. $6\frac{1}{8} = \frac{49}{8} = \frac{98}{16}$

13. $\frac{40}{16} = 2\frac{8}{16}\ (= 2\frac{1}{2})$ Luka has 2 complete puzzles.

14. $5\frac{3}{4} = \frac{23}{4}$ Sukki can fill 23 cups.

15. $2\frac{1}{2} = 2\frac{4}{8} = \frac{20}{8}$ Katie can make 20 decorations.

16. $\frac{18}{5} = 3\frac{3}{5}$ Tim has chopped 3 whole logs.

Tenths, hundredths, thousandths

1.	0·386	3 tenths	8 hundredths	6 thousandths
2.	1·725	7 tenths	2 hundredths	5 thousandths
3.	2·868	8 tenths	6 hundredths	8 thousandths
4.	3·079	0 tenths	7 hundredths	9 thousandths
5.	1·908	9 tenths	0 hundredths	8 thousandths
6.	7·357	3 tenths	5 hundredths	7 thousandths
7.	4·15	1 tenth	5 hundredths	0 thousandths
8.	6·002	0 tenths	0 hundredths	2 thousandths
9.	3·308	3 tenths	0 hundredths	8 thousandths
10.	9·167	1 tenth	6 hundredths	7 thousandths
11.	4·039	0 tenths	3 hundredths	9 thousandths
12.	2·776	7 tenths	7 hundredths	6 thousandths
13.	1·307	3 tenths	0 hundredths	7 thousandths

14. 0·304 m   15. 0·246 m   16. 0·561 m   17. 0·039 m   18. 0·438 m

19. 0·222 m   20. 0·072 m   21. 0·089 m   22. 0·068 m

Tenths, hundredths, thousandths

1. $\frac{9}{1000}$ litre = 9 ml   2. $\frac{9}{1000}$ litre = 9 ml   3. $\frac{9}{100}$ litre = 9 cl

4. $\frac{9}{1000}$ litre = 9 ml   5. $\frac{9}{10}$ litre = 9 dl   6. $\frac{9}{100}$ litre = 9 cl

ℓ   0·409 l = 409 ml = 40·9 cl   0·219 l = 219 ml = 21·9 cl

    0·493 l = 493 ml = 49·3 cl   0·039 l = 39 ml = 3·9 cl

    0·924 l = 924 ml = 92·4 cl   0·393 l = 393 ml = 39·3 cl

Number Textbook 1

7. 8 g = 0·008 kg   **8.** 62 g = 0·062 kg   **9.** 20 g = 0·02 kg
10. 300 g = 0·3 kg   **11.** 500 g = 0·5 kg   **12.** 670 g = 0·67 kg
13. 31 g = 0·031 kg   **14.** 87 g = 0·087 kg   **15.** 4 g = 0·004 kg

---

page 71   Fractions/decimals **N22**
Ordering decimals

1. 1·305 m   1·35 m   1·503 m   **2.** 0·602 m   0·62 m   0·629 m
3. 0·009 m   0·01 m   0·901 m   **4.** 4·004 m   4·04 m   4·104 m
5. 0·033 m   0·303 m   0·33 m   **6.** 1·001 m   1·01 m   1·101 m
7. 2·34 m   2·403 m   2·43 m   **8.** 0·071 m   0·17 m   0·171 m
9. 4·4 m   4·406 m   4·64 m   **10.** 5·092 m   5·29 m   5·92 m

Explore

The 3-place decimal numbers between 1·5 and 1·6 are:

1·501	1·511	1·521............................1·581	1·591
1·502	1·512	1·522............................1·582	1·592
⋮			
1·509	1·519	1·529............................1·589	1·599

There are 90 3-place decimals (9 + 9 + 9 + ... + 9 + 9 = 10 × 9 = 90)
Of these 90, 18 (1 + 1 + 1 + ... + 1 + 9 = 18) contain a digit 9

---

page 72   Fractions/decimals **N22**
Mixed problems

1. 15 × 99 = 1485   16 × 99 = 1584   17 × 99 = 1683
18 × 99 = 1782   19 × 99 = 1881   20 × 99 = 1980
The first two digits of the answers are 1 less than the multiplier; the second
two digits are the difference between the multiplier and 100.
The pattern works for all multipliers less than or equal to 100.

2. 2 weeks = 14 days   £18 × 14 = £252   £500 − £252 − £112 = £136
£136 ÷ 14 ≈ £9·71   Davinder has about £9·71 to spend each day.

3. 1 + 2 + 3 + 4 + 5 + 6 + 7 + 8 + 9 + 10 + 11 + 12 = 78 laps in 12 days
4 weeks = 7 days × 4 = 28 days   28 − 12 = 16 days remaining
12 laps × 16 = 192 laps   Total laps = 78 + 192 = 270 laps
Sally runs 270 laps in her first 4 weeks of training.

4. The final number is always one less than starting number.

5. $45 \times 45 = 2025$ $55 \times 55 = 3025$ $65 \times 65 = 4225$

6. June has 30 days.
$5 \text{ km} \times 30 = 150 \text{ km}$ Fewest number of kilometres Matthew could walk is 150 km.
$8 \text{ km} \times 30 = 240 \text{ km}$ Largest number of kilometres Matthew could walk is 240 km.
$6.2 \text{ km} \times 14 \text{ days} = 86.8 \text{ km}$
$150 \text{ km} - 86.8 \text{ km} = 63.2 \text{ km}$ Matthew must walk Poppy 63.2 further to do the minimum distance for June.

Number Textbook 2

Adding 4-digit numbers

1. $6348 + 4752 + 8196 = 19\,296$
2. $1039 + 7465 + 3211 = 11\,715$
3. $2163 + 4819 + 5642 = 12\,624$
4. $3819 + 6213 + 5784 = 15\,816$
5. $8466 + 2553 + 4032 = 15051$
6. $1194 + 7236 + 6313 = 14\,743$
7. $5217 + 6183 + 4619 = 16\,019$
8. $8129 + 9304 + 4520 = 21\,953$
9. $3789 + 8031 + 2264 = 14\,084$
10. $6520 + 8100 + 7614 = 22\,234$
11. $1297 + 5839 + 4112 = 11\,248$
12. $7183 + 2960 + 1706 = 11\,849$
13. $4919 + 6027 + 8445 = 19\,391$

@ $25\,000 - 22234 = 2766$
$25\,000 - 11248 = 13752$
$25\,000 - 11849 = 13151$
$25\,000 - 19391 = 5609$

Adding 4-digit numbers

1. $387 + 1756 + 1083 = 3226$ km
2. $1471 + 3067 + 1093 = 5631$ km
3. $2760 + 700 + 387 = 3847$ km
4. $1083 + 3067 + 3026 = 7176$ km
5. $2760 + 1093 + 3067 = 6920$ km
6. $1083 + 1349 + 700 = 3132$ km
7. $1471 + 3067 + 3026 = 7564$ km

@ shortest journey 10 520 km
e.g. New York → Toronto → Chicago → Seattle → San Francisco →
Mexico City → New Orleans → Miami

8. $2481 + 9782 + 7658 = 19\,921$
9. $9104 + 6532 + 7185 = 22\,821$
10. $4377 + 2684 + 3983 = 11\,044$
11. $1865 + 8912 + 4738 = 15\,515$

Adding 4- and 5-digit numbers

1. $8274 + 9856 = 18\,130$
2. $5717 + 4135 = 9852$
3. $13\,098 + 11\,963 = 25\,061$
4. $27\,694 + 8274 = 35\,968$
5. $9856 + 27\,694 = 37\,550$
6. $8274 + 13\,098 + 4135 = 25\,507$
7. $5717 + 27\,694 + 11\,963 = 45\,374$
8. $13\,098 + 9856 + 27\,694 = 50\,648$
9. $4135 + 5717 + 11\,963 = 21\,815$
10. $5717 + 13\,098 + 27\,694 = 46\,509$
11. $8274 + 27\,694 + 9856 = 45\,824$

Number Textbook 2

☮ 27 694 – 8274 = 19 420   more than Fizzo
     27 694 – 5717 = 21 977   more than Popo
     27 694 – 4135 = 23 559   more than Gulps
     27 694 – 13 098 = 14 596   more than Imp
     27 694 – 9856 = 17 838   more than Turbo
     27 694 – 11 963 = 15 731   more than Spangle

12. 1478 + 63 921 = 65 399
13. 3182 + 10 643 = 13 825
14. 1532 + 4618 = 6150
15. 3810 + 6438 = 10 248
16. 6411 + 23 792 = 30 203
17. 3925 + 74 219 = 78 144
18. 18 290 + 4864 = 23 154
19. 2931 + 17 824 = 20 755
20. 78 361 + 4899 = 83 260

---

page 6
Adding 4- and 5-digit numbers
    Addition/subtraction   N23

1. 1873 + 947 = £2820
2. 27 563 + 1562 = £29 125
3. 468 + 1137 = £1605
4. 32 984 + 2462 = £35 446
5. 19 608 + 1137 = £20 745
6. 27 563 + 1137 + 32 984 = £61 684
7. 2462 + 1873 + 1137 = £5472
8. 19 608 + 1562 + 27 563 = £48 733
9. 947 + 2462 + 19 608 = £23 017
10. 1137 + 19 608 + 1873 = £22 618
11. 27 563 + 1137 + 468 + 2462 = £31 630
12. 32 984 + 27 563 + 1562 + 1873 = £63 982
13. 947 + 1137 + 19 608 + 1873 = £23 565

☮ Children's answers will vary.

Explore
Either   57 986 + 1234 = 59 220 or 52 431 + 6789 = 59 220

---

page 7
Adding decimals
    Addition/subtraction   N24

1. 6·87 + 4·38 + 3·42 + 3·42 = 18·09 m
2. 4·89 + 9·11 + 6·16 + 6·16 = 26·32 m
3. 5·23 + 4·64 + 7·09 = 16·96 m
4. 5·68 + 6·39 + 8·21 = 20·28 m
5. 5·89 + 3·09 + 3·24 + 4·72 = 16·94 m
6. 3·16 + 3·02 + 4·54 + 2·97 + 4·84 = 18·53 m

Number Textbook 2

7. $5·24 + 6·89 + 2·37 + 7·32 = 21·82$ m
8. $2·42 + 1·71 + 2·39 + 3·19 + 2·34 = 12·05$ m
9. $9·03 + 4·22 + 7·43 + 6·11 = 26·79$ m

⊘ Children's answers will vary (dimensions must add to 7·91 m).
  e.g. 7·90 m by 0·01 m   or 3·95 m by 3·96 m

10. $1·48 + 2·63 + 4·12 = 8·23$
12. $6·14 + 2·96 + 7·53 = 16·63$
14. $2·13 + 8·21 + 3·65 = 13·99$

11. $3·24 + 1·58 + 2·32 = 7·14$
13. $3·39 + 5·34 + 1·27 = 10·00$

---

page 8
Adding decimals

1. £5·38 + £2·56 + £2·08 = £10·02
2. £1·99 + £3·29 + £4·63 = £9·91
3. £2·08 + £5·38 + £5·70 = £13·16
4. £5·70 + £1·99 + £2·56 = £10·25
5. £3·29 + £2·56 + £4·63 = £10·48
6. £4·63 + £5·70 + £2·08 = £12·41
7. £5·38 + £4·63 + £1·99 = £12·00
8. £2·08 + £1·99 + £3·29 = £7·36
9. £5·70 + £2·08 + £2·56 = £10·34

⊘ £20·00 − £10·02 = £9·98
  £20·00 − £13·16 = £6·84
  £20·00 − £10·48 = £9·52
  £20·00 − £12·00 = £8·00
  £20·00 − £10·34 = £9·66

  £20·00 − £9·91 = £10·09
  £20·00 − £10·25 = £9·75
  £20·00 − £12·41 = £7·59
  £20·00 − £7·36 = £12·64

10. $21·6 + 5·32 + 0·9 = 27·82$
12. $1·3 + 12·71 + 0·5 = 14·51$
14. $11·3 + 6·27 + 2·43 = 20·00$
16. $0·28 + 31·4 + 7·9 = 39·58$

11. $19·3 + 0·8 + 1·27 = 21·37$
13. $0·31 + 7·06 + 42 = 49·37$
15. $13·8 + 11·04 + 0·63 = 25·47$
17. $3·98 + 1·7 + 14·3 = 19·98$

---

page 9
Adding decimals

1. $16·56 + 21·48 + 43·51 = 81·55$ s
2. $24·25 + 19·92 + 31·75 = 75·92$ s
3. $21·48 + 19·92 + 43·51 = 84·91$ s
4. $36·29 + 21·48 + 19·92 = 77·69$ s
5. $16·56 + 31·75 + 36·29 = 84·60$ s
6. $24·25 + 36·29 + 19·92 = 80·46$ s
7. $43·51 + 21·48 + 31·75 = 96·74$ s
8. $19·92 + 36·29 + 16·56 = 72·77$ s
9. $16·56 + 21·48 + 19·92 = 57·96$ s
10. $24·25 + 21·48 + 31·75 = 77·48$ s
11. $31·75 + 19·92 + 21·48 = 73·15$ s
12. $43·51 + 36·29 + 24·25 = 104·05$ s

Number Textbook 2

Explore

There are numerous possible additions which round to each number.
For example, additions whose totals round to 4 are:

1·35	1·35	1·34	1·34	1·36	1·36
+ 2·46	+ 2·64	+ 2·56	+ 2·65	+ 2·45	+ 2·54
3·81	3·99	3·90	3·99	3·81	3·90

1·43	1·43	1·45	1·45	1·46	1·46
+ 2·56	+ 2·65	+ 2·36	+ 2·63	+ 2·35	+ 2·53
3·99	4·08	3·81	4·08	3·81	3·99

Additions whose totals round to 5 are:

1·24	1·24	1·25	1·25	1·26	1·26
+ 3·56	+ 3·65	+ 3·64	+ 3·46	+ 3·45	+ 3·54
4·8	4·89	4·89	4·71	4·71	4·80

1·45	1·45	1·46	1·46	1·52	1·52
+ 3·26	+ 3·62	+ 3·25	+ 3·52	+ 3·46	+ 3·64
4·71	5·07	4·71	4·98	4·98	5·16

There are 24 additions whose totals round to 6.
There are only 5 additions whose totals round to 12.

6·12	6·13	6·23	6·24	6·34
+ 5·43	+ 5·42	+ 5·41	+ 5·31	+ 5·21
11·55	11·55	11·64	11·55	11·55

---

page 10   Addition/subtraction   **N24**
Adding decimals

1. $2·47 + 3·49 + 6·48 = 12·44$ km
2. $3·49 + 7·42 + 6·35 = 17·26$ km
3. $3·81 + 5·35 + 6·77 = 15·93$ km
4. $9·86 + 5·17 + 7·43 = 22·46$ km
5. $6·45 + 4·38 + 7·84 = 18·67$ km
6. $4·65 + 7·29 + 1·89 = 13·83$ km
7. $8·62 + 6·38 + 7·84 = 22·84$ km
8. $9·37 + 5·63 + 4·88 = 19·88$ km
9. $5·96 + 4·74 + 3·18 = 13·88$ km
10. $8·37 + 6·18 + 4·67 = 19·22$ km
11. £44·87 + £19·85 + £34·64 = £99·36   £100 − £99·36 = £0·64   64p left
12. $1·53 + 0·98 + 1·37 = 3·88$ litres
     Blue: $2·0 − 1·53 = 0·47$ litres left
     Yellow: $2·0 − 0·98 = 1·02$ litres left
     White: $2·0 − 1·37 = 0·63$ litres left

Number Textbook 2

Subtracting 4-digit numbers

1. $6852 - 4228 = 2624$
2. $4381 - 2167 = 2214$
3. $5555 - 2348 = 3207$
4. $7641 - 2433 = 5208$
5. $6820 - 1471 = 5349$
6. $8435 - 6416 = 2019$
7. $9384 - 7228 = 2156$
8. $6428 - 4119 = 2309$
9. $5873 - 2466 = 3407$

@

1. $2624 \rightarrow 2600$
2. $2214 \rightarrow 2200$
3. $3207 \rightarrow 3200$
4. $5208 \rightarrow 5200$
5. $5349 \rightarrow 5300$
6. $2019 \rightarrow 2000$
7. $2156 \rightarrow 2200$
8. $2309 \rightarrow 2300$
9. $3407 \rightarrow 3400$

10. $6753 - 3124 = 3629$ kg
11. $5743 - 3962 = 1781$ kg
12. $7428 - 3230 = 4198$ kg
13. $4237 - 2411 = 1826$ kg
14. $6982 - 4568 = 2414$ kg
15. $8257 - 4163 = 4094$ kg

@

10. $10\,000 - 3124 = 6876$ kg
11. $10\,000 - 3962 = 6038$ kg
12. $10\,000 - 3230 = 6770$ kg
13. $10\,000 - 2411 = 7589$ kg
14. $10\,000 - 4568 = 5432$ kg
15. $10\,000 - 4163 = 5837$ kg

Subtracting 4- and 5-digit numbers

1. £9611 − £8640 = £971
2. £9611 − £7527 = £2084
3. £11 213 − £9611 = £1602
4. £19 521 − £9611 = £9910
5. £8640 − £7527 = £1113
6. £11 213 − £8640 = £2573
7. £19 521 − £8640 = £10 881
8. £11 213 − £7527 = £3686
9. £19 521 − £7527 = £11 994
10. £19 521 − £11 213 = £8308

11. $12\,604 - 9156 = 3448$
12. $13\,811 - 11\,467 = 2344$
13. $10\,418 - 7526 = 2892$
14. $15\,724 - 13\,633 = 2091$
15. $14\,249 - 8356 = 5893$
16. $18\,942 - 9753 = 9189$
17. $17\,881 - 15\,915 = 1966$
18. $14\,431 - 8562 = 5869$
19. $13\,806 - 7624 = 6182$

Subtracting 5-digit numbers

1. $44\,750 - 35\,800 = 8950$ children
2. $29\,343 - 22\,557 = 6786$ children
3. $21\,653 - 17\,584 = 4069$ children
4. $28\,334 - 21\,447 = 6887$ children
5. $26\,950 - 21\,672 = 5278$ children
6. $31\,163 - 23\,683 = 7480$ children
7. $32\,101 - 25\,680 = 6421$ children
8. $39\,707 - 29\,788 = 9919$ children
9. $20\,628 - 15\,883 = 4745$ children
10. $28\,232 - 19\,762 = 8470$ children

Number Textbook 2

@

$35\,800 - 8950 = 26\,850$ $22\,557 - 6786 = 15\,771$ $17\,584 - 4069 = 13\,515$
$21\,447 - 6887 = 14\,560$ $21\,672 - 5278 = 16\,394$ $23\,683 - 7480 = 16\,203$
$25\,680 - 6421 = 19\,259$ $29\,788 - 9919 = 19\,869$ $15\,883 - 4745 = 11\,138$
$19\,762 - 8470 = 11\,292$

Explore

The palindromic years between 1000 and 3000 are:

1001	1111	1221	1331	1441	1551	1661	1771	1881	1991
2002	2112	2222	2332	2442	2552	2662	2772	2882	2992

The difference between consecutive pairs is always 110 within the same century, but $2002 - 1991 = 11$.

There are 3 palindromic dates between 2000 and 2005:
10 11 01   20 11 02   30 11 03
The difference between consecutive pairs 100 001.

---

page 14
Subtracting 4- and 5-digit numbers

1. $1926 + 410 = 2336$ $3926 - 2336 = 1590$ £1590 left
2. $825 + 4216 = 5041$ $16\,450 - 5041 = 11\,409$ £11 409 left
3. $458 + 7456 = 7914$ $39\,451 - 7914 = 31\,537$ £31 537 left
4. $456 + 1907 = 2363$ $9831 - 2363 = 7468$ £7468 left
5. $6083 + 432 = 6515$ $27\,327 - 6515 = 20\,812$ £20 812 left
6. $819 + 4397 = 5216$ $40\,666 - 5216 = 35\,450$ £35 450 left
7. $3475 - 2986 = 489$ Cindy has 489 more.
   Cindy has £0·05 × 489 = £24·45 more.
   Together they have $3475 + 2986 = 6461$ coins worth
   £0·05 × 6461 = £323·05.
8. $19\,364 - 7498 = 11\,866$ 11 866 are hardbacks.
   $19\,364 - 6689 = 12\,675$ 12 675 are not children's books.

---

page 15
Subtracting decimals

1. $3·25 - 1·76 = 1·49$ 2. $2·35 - 1·89 = 0·46$ 3. $2·41 - 1·68 = 0·73$
4. $3·72 - 0·89 = 2·83$ 5. $2·68 - 1·93 = 0·75$ 6. $4·51 - 2·78 = 1·73$
7. $7·21 - 4·85 = 2·36$ 8. $3·18 - 1·74 = 1·44$ 9. $4·09 - 2·68 = 1·41$
10. $5·27 - 3·78 = 1·49$ 11. $1·38 - 0·92 = 0·46$ 12. $7·92 - 2·43 = 5·49$

Number Textbook 2

13. $4.32 - 1.86 = 2.46$ 2.46 litres left
14. $5.43 - 2.87 = 2.56$ 2.56 litres left
15. $6.17 - 3.94 = 2.23$ 2.23 litres left
16. $8.29 - 2.86 = 5.43$ 5.43 litres left
17. $4.35 - 1.56 = 2.79$ 2.79 litres left
18. $2.13 - 0.59 = 1.54$ 1.54 litres left
19. $3.44 - 2.51 = 0.93$ 0.93 litres left
20. $8.19 - 4.25 = 3.94$ 3.94 litres left

ⓔ
13. $2.46 - 0.71 = 1.75$ 1.75 litres left
14. $2.56 - 0.71 = 1.85$ 1.85 litres left
15. $2.23 - 0.71 = 1.52$ 1.52 litres left
16. $5.43 - 0.71 = 4.72$ 4.72 litres left
17. $2.79 - 0.71 = 2.08$ 2.08 litres left
18. $1.54 - 0.71 = 0.83$ 0.83 litres left
19. $0.93 - 0.71 = 0.22$ 0.22 litres left
20. $3.94 - 0.71 = 3.23$ 3.23 litres left

Subtracting decimals

1. $35.48 - 4.79 = 30.69$ s
2. $24.43 - 3.56 = 20.87$ s
3. $46.12 - 5.33 = 40.79$ s
4. $37.25 - 3.47 = 33.78$ s
5. $53.71 - 2.83 = 50.88$ s
6. $22.14 - 1.8 = 20.34$ s
7. $47.33 - 6.46 = 40.87$ s
8. $58.64 - 5.75 = 52.89$ s
9. $34.12 - 3.27 = 30.85$ s

Explore

Answers will vary.
Some examples include:

$$\begin{array}{r} 23.85 \\ -\ 14.76 \\ \hline 9.09 \end{array} \qquad \begin{array}{r} 45.27 \\ -\ 36.18 \\ \hline 9.09 \end{array}$$

Number Textbook 2

Subtracting decimals

1. £5·26 – £1·59 = £3·67
2. £6·28 – £2·76 = £3·52
3. £2·23 – £1·38 = £0·85
4. £15·72 – £4·88 = £10·84
5. £11·54 – £5·75 = £5·79
6. £8·27 – £1·69 = £6·58
7. £9·48 – £3·78 = £5·70
8. £26·31 – £10·85 = £15·46
9. £7·05 – £2·55 = £4·50
10. £35·25 – £11·65 = £23·60
11. £15·41 – £6·94 = £8·47
12. £12·34 – £1·88 = £10·46
13. £11·22 – £2·39 = £8·83

Explore

Answers will vary.

Subtracting decimals

1. 3·16 – 1·69 = 1·47 m
2. 4·69 – 1·93 = 2·76 m
3. 1·23 – 0·85 = 0·38 m
4. 1·41 – 0·65 = 0·76 m
5. 2·32 – 1·59 = 0·73 m
6. 3·06 – 1·83 = 1·23 m

7. 42·2 – 8·9 = 33·3
8. 42·2 – 9·48 = 32·72
9. 42·2 – 2·56 = 39·64
10. 29·32 – 8·9 = 20·42
11. 29·32 – 9·48 = 19·84
12. 29·32 – 2·56 = 26·76
13. 35·43 – 8·9 = 26·53
14. 35·43 – 9·48 = 25·95
15. 35·43 – 2·56 = 32·87

16. £6·66 + £0·99 + £4·88 = £12·53   £15·41 – £12·53 = £2·88 left
£2·88 – £1·50 = £1·38 when she gets home
17. 7·45 – 3·87 = 3·58   Bean has grown 3·58 cm, 1·79 cm per day

---

Factors

1. 10:   1, 10   2, 5
2. 18:   1, 18   2, 9   3, 6
3. 25:   1, 25   5, 5
4. 26:   1, 26   2, 13
5. 55:   1, 55   5, 11
6. 64:   1, 64   2, 32   4, 16   8, 8
7. 60:   1, 60   2, 30   3, 20   4, 15   5, 12   6, 10
8. 48:   1, 48   2, 24   3, 16   4, 12   6, 8
9. 81:   1, 81   3, 27   9, 9
10. 31:   1, 31

Number Textbook 2

◉

1. factors of 10:   1, 2, 5, 10
2. factors of 18:   1, 2, 3, 6, 9, 18
3. factors of 25:   1, 5, 25
4. factors of 26:   1, 2, 13, 26
5. factors of 55:   1, 5, 11, 55
6. factors of 64:   1, 2, 4, 8, 16, 32, 64
7. factors of 60:   1, 2, 3, 4, 5, 6, 10, 12, 15, 20, 30, 60
8. factors of 48:   1, 2, 3, 4, 6, 8, 12, 16, 24, 48
9. factors of 81:   1, 3, 9, 27, 81
10. factors of 31:   1, 31

11. $15 = 1 \times 15 = 3 \times 5$
12. $36 = 1 \times 36 = 2 \times 18 = 3 \times 12 = 4 \times 9 = 6 \times 6$
13. $102 = 1 \times 102 = 2 \times 51 = 3 \times 34 = 6 \times 17$
14. $96 = 1 \times 96 = 2 \times 48 = 3 \times 32 = 4 \times 24 = 6 \times 16 = 8 \times 12$
15. $108 = 1 \times 108 = 2 \times 54 = 3 \times 36 = 4 \times 27 = 6 \times 18 = 9 \times 12$
16. $200 = 1 \times 200 = 2 \times 100 = 4 \times 50 = 5 \times 40 = 8 \times 25 = 10 \times 20$
17. $118 = 1 \times 118 = 2 \times 59$
18. $220 = 1 \times 220 = 2 \times 110 = 4 \times 55 = 5 \times 44 = 10 \times 22 = 11 \times 20$
19. $56 = 1 \times 56 = 2 \times 28 = 4 \times 14 = 7 \times 8$
20. $72 = 1 \times 72 = 2 \times 36 = 3 \times 24 = 4 \times 18 = 6 \times 12 = 8 \times 9$
21. $232 = 1 \times 232 = 2 \times 116 = 4 \times 58 = 8 \times 29$

11a. factors of 15:   1, 3, 5, 15
12a. factors of 36:   1, 2, 3, 4, 6, 9, 12, 18, 36
13a. factors of 102:   1, 2, 3, 6, 17, 34, 51, 102
14a. factors of 96:   1, 2, 3, 4, 6, 8, 12, 16, 24, 32, 48, 96
15a. factors of 108:   1, 2, 3, 4, 6, 9, 12, 18, 27, 36, 54, 108
16a. factors of 200:   1, 2, 4, 5, 8, 10, 20, 25, 40, 50, 100, 200
17a. factors of 118:   1, 2, 59, 118
18a. factors of 220:   1, 2, 4, 5, 10, 11, 20, 22, 44, 55, 110, 220
19a. factors of 56:   1, 2, 4, 7, 8, 14, 28, 56
20a. factors of 72:   1, 2, 3, 4, 6, 8, 9, 12, 18, 24, 36, 72
21a. factors of 232:   1, 2, 4, 8, 29, 58, 116, 232

Number Textbook 2

Factors

1. factors of 98: 2, 7, 14   factors of 99: 3, 9, 11   factors of 100: 2, 4, 5
   factors of 101: none   factors of 102: 2, 3, 17
2. factors of 121: none   factors of 124: 2, 4, 31   factors of 125: 5
   factors of 126: 3, 9, 14, 18, 21,   factors of 127: none
3. factors of 132: 2, 3, 4, 11, 12   factors of 133: 19
   factors of 134: 2
   factors of 135: 3, 5, 15, 27
   factors of 136: 2, 4, 34
4. factors of 40: 1, 2, 4, 5, 8, 10, 20, 40
5. 48: 1, 2, 3, 4, 6, 8, 12, 16, 24, 48
6. 64: 1, 2, 4, 8, 16, 32, 64
7. 81: 1, 3, 9, 27, 81
8. 72: 1, 2, 3, 4, 6, 8, 9, 12, 18, 24, 36, 72

ℯ
Answers will vary.

Factors

no of factors	
1	1
2	2, 3, 5, 7, 11, 13, 17, 19, 23, 29, 31, 37, 39, 41, 43, 47, 53, 57, 59
3	4, 9, 25, 49
4	6, 8, 10, 14, 15, 21, 22, 26, 27, 33, 34, 35, 38, 46, 51, 55, 58
5	16
6	12, 18, 20, 28, 42, 44, 45, 52, 54
7	
8	24, 30, 32, 40, 50, 56
9	36
10	48
11	
12	60

Number Textbook 2

1. factors of 120: 1, 2, 3, 4, 5, 6, 8, 10, 12, 15, 20, 24, 30, 40, 60, 120
2. factors of 150: 1, 2, 3, 5, 6, 10, 15, 25, 30, 50, 75, 150
3. factors of 111: 1, 3, 37, 111
4. factors of 121: 1, 11, 121
5. factors of 144: 1, 2, 3, 4, 6, 8, 9, 12, 16, 18, 24, 36, 48, 72, 144
6. factors of 101: 1, 101
7. factors of 200: 1, 2, 4, 5, 8, 10, 20, 25, 40, 50, 100, 200

Explore

The first three perfect numbers are 6, 28, 496.

Prime numbers

1. 35 is not prime   factors: 1, 5, 7, 35
2. 9 is not prime   factors: 1, 3, 9
3. 27 is not prime   factors: 1, 3, 9, 27
4. 33 is not prime   factors: 1, 3, 11, 33
5. 9 is not prime   factors: 1, 3, 9
6. 21 is not prime   factors: 1, 3, 7, 21
7. 99 is not prime   factors: 1, 3, 9, 11, 33, 99
8. 105 is not prime   factors: 1, 3, 5, 7, 15, 21, 35, 105

1	2	3	4	5	6
7	8	9	10	11	12
13	14	15	16	17	18
19	20	21	22	23	24
25	26	27	28	29	30
31	32	33	34	35	36
37	38	39	40	41	42
43	44	45	46	47	48
49	50	51	52	53	54
55	56	57	58	59	60

Number Textbook 2

Prime numbers

1.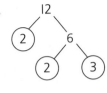

2.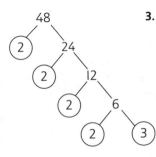

3.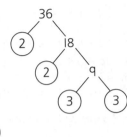

4.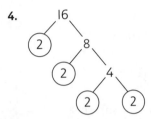

5.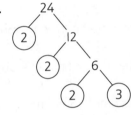

6.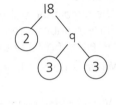

1a. $12 = 2 \times 2 \times 3$

2a. $48 = 2 \times 2 \times 2 \times 2 \times 3$

3a. $36 = 2 \times 2 \times 3 \times 3$

4a. $16 = 2 \times 2 \times 2 \times 2$

5a. $24 = 2 \times 2 \times 2 \times 3$

6a. $18 = 2 \times 3 \times 3$

Prime number	Difference
2	1
3	2
5	2
7	4
11	2
13	4
17	2
19	4
23	6
29	2
31	6
37	4
41	2

Prime number	Difference
43	4
47	6
53	6
59	2
61	6
67	4
71	2
73	6
79	4
83	6
89	8
97	–

Twin primes

3 and 5
5 and 7
11 and 13
17 and 19
29 and 31
41 and 43
59 and 61
71 and 73

Number Textbook 2

page 24
Prime numbers

1. $20 = 1 + 19 = 3 + 17 = 7 + 13$
2. $34 = 3 + 31 = 5 + 29 = 11 + 23 = 17 + 17$
3. $24 = 5 + 19 = 7 + 17 = 11 + 13$
4. $36 = 5 + 31 = 7 + 29 = 13 + 23 = 17 + 19$
5. $42 = 3 + 39 = 5 + 37 = 11 + 31 = 13 + 29 = 19 + 23$
6. $30 = 7 + 23 = 11 + 19 = 13 + 17$

7.–12. Answers will vary.

ℯ Answers will vary.

Explore

The remainder is always 1.
Prime numbers greater than 3 are all 'next to' multiples of 6,
i.e. either $6n + 1$ or $6n - 1$.

When squared, they become:
$$(6n + 1)^2 = 36n^2 + 12n + 1$$
$$(6n - 1)^2 = 36n^2 - 12n + 1$$

When divided by 12, they become: $3n^2 + n + \frac{1}{12}$ or $3n^2 - n + \frac{1}{12}$

The remainder is always 1.

---

page 25
Positive and negative numbers

1. ⁻35, ⁻5, 5	2. ⁻11, 2, 41	3. ⁻4, ⁻1, 34	4. ⁻2, 13, 20
5. ⁻22, ⁻1, 21	6. ⁻50, ⁻15, 0	7. ⁻14, 4, 46	8. ⁻22, ⁻12, ⁻9
9. ⁻38, 0, 8	10. ⁻37, ⁻27, 47		

11. **a** 0°C **b** 6°C **c** ⁻3°C **d** ⁻1°C **e** ⁻2°C
12. **a** 6°C **b** 3°C **c** 10°C **d** 12°C **e** 8°C
    f 6°C **g** 9°C

ℯ

11.

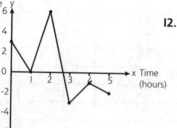

12.

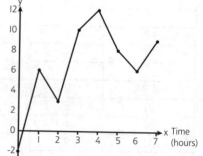

Number Textbook 2

page 26

Positive and negative numbers

I. d = 28   **2.** d = 25   **3.** d = 39   **4.** d = 38   **5.** d = 66
6. d = 12   **7.** d = 86   **8.** d = 34   **9.** d = 34   **10.** d = 103

II. 90 km   **12.** 100 km   **13.** 40 km   **14.** 40 km
15. 100 km   **16.** 90 km   **17.** 130 km   **18.** 90 km

page 27

Positive and negative numbers

I. £4·25 − £6·82 = ⁻£2·57
2. £7·83 − £2·19 = £5·64
3. £3·61 − £5·92 = ⁻£2·31
4. £1·48 − £2·09 = ⁻£0·61
5. £8·12 − £3·05 = £5·07
6. £1·11 − £7·51 = ⁻£6·40
7. £5·80 − £10·07 = ⁻£4·27
8. £7·16 − £8·66 = ⁻£1·50
9. £6·06 − £4·33 = £1·73
10. £9·47 − £7·20 = £2·27
II. £5·99 − £7·22 = ⁻£1·23
12. £6·53 − £11·84 = ⁻£5·31
13. £0 − £5·09 = ⁻£5·09

e

I. ⁻£2·57 + £4·25 = £1·68
2. £5·64 + £4·25 = £9·89
3. ⁻£2·31 + £4·25 = £1·94
4. ⁻£0·61 + £4·25 = £3·64
5. £5·07 + £4·25 = £9·32
6. ⁻£6·40 + £4·25 = ⁻£2·15
7. ⁻£4·27 + £4·25 = ⁻£0·02
8. ⁻£1·50 + £4·25 = £2·75
9. £1·73 + £4·25 = £5·98
10. £2·27 + £4·25 = £6·52
II. ⁻£1·23 + £4·25 = £3·02
12. ⁻£5·31 + £4·25 = ⁻£1·06
13. ⁻£5·09 + £4·25 = ⁻£0·84

14. ⁻12°C − 3°C = ⁻15°C   3°C × 3 = 9°C   ⁻15°C + 9°C = ⁻6°C
15. difference between ⁻3 and 6 = 9   temperature must rise 9°C
    9 ÷ 0·5 = 18   18 × 20 minutes = 6 hours

page 28

Rounding and estimating

I. 39 → 40
2. 467 → 470
3. 5394 → 5390
4. 471 → 500
5. 6325 → 6300
6. 58 476 → 58 500
7. 2613 → 3000
8. 3700 → 4000
9. 45 617 → 46 000
10. 7·7 → 8
II. 6·39 → 6
12. 4·156 → 4
13. 8·37 → 8·4
14. 4·093 → 4·1
15. 16·19 → 16·2

Number Textbook 2

16. 400×20 a
18. $50 + 300$ a
20. $6000 \div 10$ b
22. $800 \div 6$ a

17. 40×40 c
19. $360 - 20$ b
21. $400 \div 7$ a

🄮

16. $417 \times 22 = 9174$
18. $49 \cdot 61 + 328 \cdot 2 = 377 \cdot 81$
20. $5658 \div 11 \cdot 5 = 492$
22. $\frac{1}{6}$ of $782 \cdot 1 = 130 \cdot 35$

17. $39 \times 41 = 1599$
19. $358 \cdot 6 - 17 \cdot 8 = 340 \cdot 8$
21. $377 \div 6 \cdot 5 = 58$

---

page 29
Estimating

Place-value   N30

1. double (4 cm + 3 cm) = 14 cm
2. double (4 cm + 2 cm) = 12 cm
3. double (4 cm + 4 cm) = 16 cm
4. double (5 cm + 4 cm) = 18 cm
5. double (7 cm + 3 cm) = 20 cm
6. double (7 cm + 3 cm) = 20 cm

🄮

1. $4 \text{ cm} \times 3 \text{ cm} = 12 \text{ cm}^2, 12 \cdot 528 \text{ cm}^2$
2. $4 \text{ cm} \times 2 \text{ cm} = 8 \text{ cm}^2, 8 \cdot 162 \text{ cm}^2$
3. $4 \text{ cm} \times 4 \text{ cm} = 16 \text{ cm}^2, 15 \cdot 9744 \text{ cm}^2$
4. $5 \text{ cm} \times 4 \text{ cm} = 20 \text{ cm}^2, 21 \cdot 2898 \text{ cm}^2$
5. $7 \text{ cm} \times 3 \text{ cm} = 21 \text{ cm}^2, 20 \cdot 3 \text{ cm}^2$
6. $7 \text{ cm} \times 3 \text{ cm} = 21 \text{ cm}^2, 19 \cdot 152 \text{ cm}^2$

7. $\frac{4}{5}$ of $56 = 44 \cdot 8$ **8.** $\frac{5}{6}$ of $63 = 52 \cdot 5$ **9.** $121 \cdot 7 - 48 \cdot 8 = 72 \cdot 9$

---

page 30
Estimating

Place-value   N30

1. £300 × 2 = £600   **2.** £300 × 4 = £1200   **3.** £400 × 3 = £1200
4. £500 × 5 = £2500   **5.** £500 × 3 = £1500

6. (£300 × 4) + £500 = £1700
7. (£400 × 3) + (£500 × 2) = £2200
8. (£500 × 3) + (£400 × 3) = £2700
9. £300 + £300 + £500 + £500 + £400 = £2000
10. £2000 × 2 = £4000

exact costs
1a. £318 × 2 = £636   **2a.** £287 × 4 = £1148   **3a.** £417 × 3 = £1251
4a. £516 × 5 = £2580   **5a.** £493 × 3 = £1479

Number Textbook 2

page 30 cont ...

6a. (£318 × 4) + £516 = £1788
7a. (£417 × 3) + (£516 × 2) = £2283
8a. (£516 × 3) + (£417 × 3) = £2799
9a. £318 + £287 + £516 + £493 + £417 = £2031
10a. £2031 × 2 = £4062

11. £300 × 4000 = £1 200 000   £318 × 4120 = £1 310 160
12. £300 × 6000 = £1 800 000   £287 × 6210 = £1 782 270
13. £500 × 8000 = 4 000 000   £516 × 7960 = £4 107 360
14. £400 × 3000 = £1 200 000   £417 × 3160 = £1 317 720
15. £500 × 2000 = £1 000 000   £493 × 1870 = £921 910

ⓔ

City	£1 310 160 – £750 000 = £560 160
United	£1 782 270 – £750 000 = £1 032 270
Rovers	£4 107 360 – £750 000 = £3 357 360
Rangers	£1 317 720 – £750 000 = £567 720
Town	£921 910 – £750 000 = £171 910

---

page 31
Multiplying decimals

1. 4·8 × 7 = 33·6 cm   **2.** 6·3 × 8 = 50·4 cm   **3.** 2·9 × 9 = 26·1 cm
4. 7·5 × 6 = 45 cm   **5.** 6·9 × 3 = 20·7 cm   **6.** 8·3 × 6 = 49·8 cm
7. 7·7 × 4 = 30·8 cm   **8.** 5·7 × 8 = 45·6 cm   **9.** 9·3 × 4 = 37·2 cm

10. 2 × 3·8 = 7·6   **11.** 5 × 5·9 = 29·5   **12.** 7 × 4·7 = 32·9
13. 3 × 6·2 = 18·6   **14.** 4 × 7·5 = 30   **15.** 9 × 8·3 = 74·7
16. 6 × 12·4 = 74·4   **17.** 8 × 13·7 = 109·6   **18.** 7 × 15·2 = 106·4

---

page 32
Multiplying decimals

1. 2·4 m × 8 = 19·2 m   **2.** 3·6 m × 7 = 25·2 m   **3.** 2·8 m × 6 = 16·8 m
4. 3·1 m × 11 = 34·1 m   **5.** 2·6 m × 9 = 23·4 m   **6.** 2·7 m × 7 = 18·9 m
7. 3·3 m × 9 = 29·7 m   **8.** 2·2 × 8 = 17·6   **9.** 7·6 × 3 = 22·8
10. 3·5 × 9 = 31·5   **11.** 7·6 × 6 = 45·6   **12.** 4·3 × 7 = 30·1
13. 5·7 × 7 = 39·9   **14.** 9·3 × 4 = 37·2   **15.** 1·9 × 7 = 13·3
16. 4·7 × 8 = 37·6   **17.** 7·5 × 9 = 67·5

Number Textbook 2

Multiplying decimals

1.	$3{\cdot}5\text{ m} \times 8 = 28{\cdot}0\text{ m}$	$4{\cdot}1\text{ m} \times 7 = 28{\cdot}7\text{ m}$	$4{\cdot}1\text{ m} \times 7$ gives more string
2.	$5{\cdot}9\text{ m} \times 6 = 35{\cdot}4\text{ m}$	$4{\cdot}7\text{ m} \times 8 = 37{\cdot}6\text{ m}$	$4{\cdot}7\text{ m} \times 8$ gives more string
3.	$4{\cdot}2\text{ m} \times 9 = 37{\cdot}8\text{ m}$	$6{\cdot}7\text{ m} \times 5 = 33{\cdot}5\text{ m}$	$4{\cdot}2\text{ m} \times 9$ gives more string
4.	$7{\cdot}3\text{ m} \times 4 = 29{\cdot}2\text{ m}$	$6{\cdot}8\text{ m} \times 5 = 34{\cdot}0\text{ m}$	$6{\cdot}8\text{ m} \times 5$ gives more string
5.	$9{\cdot}6\text{ m} \times 5 = 48{\cdot}0\text{ m}$	$7{\cdot}8\text{ m} \times 6 = 46{\cdot}8\text{ m}$	$9{\cdot}6\text{ m} \times 5$ gives more string
6.	$8{\cdot}1\text{ m} \times 6 = 48{\cdot}6\text{ m}$	$6{\cdot}3\text{ m} \times 8 = 50{\cdot}4\text{ m}$	$6{\cdot}3\text{ m} \times 8$ gives more string

Explore

Possibilities are:
$3 \times 9{\cdot}6 = 28{\cdot}8$ $6 \times 4{\cdot}8 = 28{\cdot}8$
$4 \times 7{\cdot}2 = 28{\cdot}8$ $8 \times 3{\cdot}6 = 28{\cdot}8$

Multiplying decimals

1. $6 \times 4{\cdot}0\text{ s} = 24{\cdot}0\text{ s}$
$6 \times 0{\cdot}3\text{ s} = \underline{\ 1{\cdot}8\text{ s}}$
$25{\cdot}8\text{ s}$

2. $4 \times 3{\cdot}0\text{ s} = 12{\cdot}0\text{ s}$
$4 \times 0{\cdot}6\text{ s} = \underline{\ 2{\cdot}4\text{ s}}$
$14{\cdot}4\text{ s}$

3. $3 \times 5{\cdot}0\text{ s} = 15{\cdot}0\text{ s}$
$3 \times 0{\cdot}1\text{ s} = \underline{\ 0{\cdot}3\text{ s}}$
$15{\cdot}3\text{ s}$

4. $9 \times 1{\cdot}0\text{ s} = \ 9{\cdot}0\text{ s}$
$9 \times 0{\cdot}9\text{ s} = \underline{\ 8{\cdot}1\text{ s}}$
$17{\cdot}1\text{ s}$

5. $7 \times 2{\cdot}0\text{ s} = 14{\cdot}0\text{ s}$
$7 \times 0{\cdot}8\text{ s} = \underline{\ 5{\cdot}6\text{ s}}$
$19{\cdot}6\text{ s}$

6. $2 \times 4{\cdot}0\text{ s} = \ 8{\cdot}0\text{ s}$
$2 \times 0{\cdot}6\text{ s} = \underline{\ 1{\cdot}2\text{ s}}$
$9{\cdot}2\text{ s}$

7. $5 \times 3{\cdot}0\text{ s} = 15{\cdot}0\text{ s}$
$5 \times 0{\cdot}7\text{ s} = \underline{\ 3{\cdot}5\text{ s}}$
$18{\cdot}5\text{ s}$

8. $8 \times 6{\cdot}0\text{ s} = 48{\cdot}0\text{ s}$
$8 \times 0{\cdot}4\text{ s} = \underline{\ 3{\cdot}2\text{ s}}$
$51{\cdot}2\text{ s}$

9. $6 \times 7{\cdot}0\text{ s} = 42{\cdot}0\text{ s}$
$6 \times 0{\cdot}8\text{ s} = \underline{\ 4{\cdot}8\text{ s}}$
$46{\cdot}8\text{ s}$

10. $8 \times 2{\cdot}0\text{ s} = 16{\cdot}0\text{ s}$
$8 \times 0{\cdot}9\text{ s} = \underline{\ 7{\cdot}2\text{ s}}$
$23{\cdot}2\text{ s}$

11. $7 \times 3{\cdot}0\text{ s} = 21{\cdot}0\text{ s}$
$7 \times 0{\cdot}8\text{ s} = \underline{\ 5{\cdot}6\text{ s}}$
$26{\cdot}6\text{ s}$

12. $4 \times 5{\cdot}0\text{ s} = 20{\cdot}0\text{ s}$
$4 \times 0{\cdot}6\text{ s} = \underline{\ 2{\cdot}4\text{ s}}$
$22{\cdot}4\text{ s}$

13. $8 \times 9{\cdot}0\text{ s} = 72{\cdot}0\text{ s}$
$8 \times 0{\cdot}7\text{ s} = \underline{\ 5{\cdot}6\text{ s}}$
$77{\cdot}6\text{ s}$

14. $5 \times 8{\cdot}0\text{ s} = 40{\cdot}0\text{ s}$
$5 \times 0{\cdot}3\text{ s} = \underline{\ 1{\cdot}5\text{ s}}$
$41{\cdot}5\text{ s}$

15. $7 \times 4{\cdot}0\text{ s} = 28{\cdot}0\text{ s}$
$7 \times 0{\cdot}9\text{ s} = \underline{\ 6{\cdot}3\text{ s}}$
$34{\cdot}3\text{ s}$

Number Textbook 2

16. $3 \times 6{\cdot}0$ s $= 18{\cdot}0$ s
$3 \times 0{\cdot}4$ s $= \underline{ 1{\cdot}2 \text{ s}}$
$\underline{19{\cdot}2 \text{ s}}$

17. $2 \times 7{\cdot}0$ s $= 14{\cdot}0$ s
$2 \times 0{\cdot}3$ s $= \underline{0{\cdot}6 \text{ s}}$
$\underline{14{\cdot}6 \text{ s}}$

18. $9 \times 9{\cdot}0$ s $= 81{\cdot}0$ s
$9 \times 0{\cdot}7$ s $= \underline{ 6{\cdot}3 \text{ s}}$
$\underline{87{\cdot}3 \text{ s}}$

19. $6 \times 8{\cdot}0$ s $= 48{\cdot}0$ s
$6 \times 0{\cdot}2$ s $= \underline{ 1{\cdot}2 \text{ s}}$
$\underline{49{\cdot}2 \text{ s}}$

---

page 35
Multiplying decimals

1. £1·86 × 4 = £7·44
4. £9·47 × 5 = £47·35
7. £3·54 × 7 = £24·78
10. £1·96 × 5 = £9·80

2. £2·99 × 6 = £17·94
5. £2·75 × 4 = £11·00
8. £4·44 × 6 = £26·64

3. £8·35 × 2 = £16·70
6. £7·59 × 3 = £22·77
9. £6·58 × 7 = £46·06

ℯ £9·47 + £2·99 + £8·35 + £2·75 + £1·96 + £6·58 + £3·54 + (£7·59 × 2) + £4·44 + (£1·86 × 2) = £58·98

11. 7 × 3·68 = 25·76
14. 9·38 × 4 = 37·52
17. 3 × 9·74 = 29·22

12. 4·32 × 7 = 30·24
15. 5 × 4·55 = 22·75

13. 8 × 5·16 = 41·28
16. 6·38 × 9 = 57·42

---

page 36
Multiplying decimals

1. 7 × £3·55 = £24·85
£50 − £24·85 = £25·15   Nazma has £25·15 left.

2. £4·63 + £2·74 + £1·98 = £9·35
£9·35 × 2 = £18·70   John has £18·70 altogether.

3. 1·46 l × 2 = 2·92 l
2·92 l × 4 = 11·68 l   Ted uses 11·68 l of petrol.

4. 8·31 m × 4 = 33·24 m
5·46 m × 6 = 32·76 m
33·24 m − 32·76 m = 0·48 m   Jeevan's train travels 48 cm further than Martha's.

Number Textbook 2

page 36 cont ...

5. $5 \times 3.75 = 18.75$
8. $3 \times 3.75 = 11.25$
11. $2 \times 3.75 = 7.5$

6. $5 \times 6.23 = 31.15$
9. $3 \times 6.23 = 18.69$
12. $2 \times 6.23 = 12.46$

7. $5 \times 4.19 = 20.95$
10. $3 \times 4.19 = 12.57$
13. $2 \times 4.19 = 8.38$

ⓔ

largest product: 31.15
smallest product: 7.5
difference $= 31.15 - 7.5 = 23.65$

Explore

There are 16 different products:

$3 \times 7.45 = 22.35$	$4 \times 5.47 = 21.88$	$5 \times 4.37 = 21.85$	$7 \times 3.45 = 24.15$
$3 \times 7.54 = 22.62$	$4 \times 5.74 = 22.96$	$5 \times 4.73 = 23.65$	$7 \times 3.54 = 24.78$
	$4 \times 7.45 = 29.8$	$5 \times 7.34 = 36.7$	$7 \times 4.35 = 30.45$
	$4 \times 7.54 = 30.16$	$5 \times 7.43 = 37.15$	$7 \times 4.53 = 31.71$
			$7 \times 5.34 = 37.38$
			$7 \times 5.43 = 38.01$

---

page 37
Dividing

1. $685 \div 5 = 137$ tickets
4. $888 \div 6 = 148$ tickets
7. $894 \div 6 = 149$ tickets
10. $696 \div 6 = 116$ tickets

2. $738 \div 9 = 82$ tickets
5. $792 \div 9 = 88$ tickets
8. $768 \div 8 = 96$ tickets

3. $889 \div 7 = 127$ tickets
6. $816 \div 8 = 102$ tickets
9. $925 \div 5 = 185$ tickets

ⓔ

1. $685 \div 4 = 171$ r 1   171 tickets
3. $889 \div 4 = 222$ r 1   222 tickets
5. $792 \div 4 = 198$ 198 tickets
7. $894 \div 4 = 223$ r 2   223 tickets
9. $925 \div 4 = 231$ r 1   231 tickets

2. $738 \div 4 = 184$ r 2   184 tickets
4. $888 \div 4 = 222$ 222 tickets
6. $816 \div 4 = 204$ 204 tickets
8. $768 \div 4 = 192$ 192 tickets
10. $696 \div 4 = 174$ 174 tickets

---

page 38
Dividing

1. $456 \div 12 = 38$
5. $507 \div 13 = 39$

2. $638 \div 11 = 58$
6. $876 \div 12 = 73$

3. $689 \div 13 = 53$
7. $871 \div 13 = 67$

4. $924 \div 11 = 84$

8. $468 \div 36 = 13$ buses
11. $546 \div 42 = 13$ buses
14. $816 \div 48 = 17$ buses

9. $308 \div 14 = 22$ buses
12. $722 \div 38 = 19$ buses
15. $936 \div 52 = 18$ buses

10. $558 \div 18 = 31$ buses
13. $416 \div 26 = 16$ buses
16. $832 \div 64 = 13$ buses

Number Textbook 2

Dividing

1. $697 \div 17 = 41$
2. $414 \div 18 = 23$
3. $608 \div 19 = 32$
4. $368 \div 23 = 16$
5. $560 \div 16 = 35$
6. $567 \div 27 = 21$
7. $588 \div 14 = 42$
8. $286 \div 22 = 13$
9. $432 \div 24 = 18$
10. $595 \div 17 = 35$
11. $672 \div 16 = 42$
12. $364 \div 13 = 28$
13. $342 \div 18 = 19$
14. $676 \div 26 = 26$

15. $735 \div 21 = 35$ 35 apples/bag $35 \times 4 = 140$ apples in 4 bags
16. Hilsea £586 $\div$ 29 = £20.20 each (with 20p left over).
    Tripton £396 $\div$ 27 = £14.66 each (with 18p left over).
17. £1000 – £280 = £720   £720 $\div$ £36 = 20 tickets
18. $544 \div 17 = 32$ Journey is 32 miles
19. $851 \div 37 = 23$ Mystery number is 37
20. $1000 - 244 = 756$ $756 \div 36 = 21$ Mystery number is 21
21. $432 \div 16 = 27$ Mean is 27 pupils per class

Dividing decimals

1. $36.5 \div 5 = 7.3$ hours
2. $40.5 \div 5 = 8.1$ hours
3. $34.5 \div 5 = 6.9$ hours
4. $38.5 \div 5 = 7.7$ hours
5. $35.5 \div 5 = 7.1$ hours
6. $41.5 \div 5 = 8.3$ hours
7. $35 \div 5 = 7$ hours
8. $37.5 \div 5 = 7.5$ hours

✏ 1. £4 $\times$ 36.5 = £146
2. £4 $\times$ 40.5 = £162
3. £4 $\times$ 34.5 = £138
4. £4 $\times$ 38.5 = £154
5. £4 $\times$ 35.5 = £142
6. £4 $\times$ 41.5 = £166
7. £4 $\times$ 35 = £140
8. £4 $\times$ 37.5 = £150

9. 61.8 g $\div$ 6 = 10.3 g
10. 52.2 g $\div$ 3 = 17.4 g
11. 49.2 g $\div$ 4 = 12.3 g
12. 93.6 g $\div$ 6 = 15.6 g
13. 80.4 g $\div$ 6 = 13.4 g
14. 74.8 g $\div$ 4 = 18.7 g
15. 95.2 g $\div$ 8 = 11.9 g
16. 69.2 g $\div$ 4 = 17.3 g
17. 97.6 g $\div$ 4 = 24.4 g
18. 23.4 g $\div$ 3 = 7.8 g

Dividing decimals

1. $49.2 \div 4 = 12.3$
2. $73.8 \div 3 = 24.6$
3. $62.8 \div 4 = 15.7$
4. $69.5 \div 5 = 13.9$
5. $87.2 \div 2 = 43.6$
6. $85.2 \div 3 = 28.4$
7. $86.8 \div 4 = 21.7$
8. $81.5 \div 5 = 16.3$
9. $94.4 \div 8 = 11.8$
10. $93.8 \div 7 = 13.4$

Number Textbook 2

page 41 cont ...

II. £7·80 ÷ 3 = £2·60 **I2.** £18·40 ÷ 4 = £4·60 **I3.** £10·80 ÷ 3 = £3·60
I4. £22·50 ÷ 5 = £4·50 **I5.** £63·20 ÷ 8 = £7·90 **I6.** £54·60 ÷ 7 = £7·80

Explore

Answers up to ÷ by 20

£19·20 ÷ 2 = £9·60   £19·20 ÷ 3 = £6·40
£19·20 ÷ 4 = £4·80   £19·20 ÷ 5 = £3·84
£19·20 ÷ 6 = £3·20   £19·20 ÷ 7 = £2·74 r 2p
£19·20 ÷ 8 = £2·40   £19·20 ÷ 9 = £2·13 r 3p
£19·20 ÷ 10 = £1·92   £19·20 ÷ 11 = £1·74 r 6p
£19·20 ÷ 12 = £1·60   £19·20 ÷ 13 = £1·47 r 9p
£19·20 ÷ 14 = £1·37 r 2p   £19·20 ÷ 15 = £1·28
£19·20 ÷ 16 = £1·20   £19·20 ÷ 17 = £1·12 r 16p
£19·20 ÷ 18 = £1·06 r 12p £19·20 ÷ 19 = £1·01 r 1p
£19·20 ÷ 20 = £0·96

page 42
Dividing decimals

I. £110·46 ÷ 6 = £18·41 **2.** £131·36 ÷ 8 = £16·42 **3.** £169·12 ÷ 7 = £24·16
4. £176·49 ÷ 9 = £19·61 **5.** £157·38 ÷ 6 = £26·23 **6.** £139·93 ÷ 7 = £19·99
7. £143·28 ÷ 8 = £17·91

Explore

2178 ÷ 2 = 1089   3267 ÷ 3 = 1089   4356 ÷ 4 = 1089

The same answer is found for:

5445 ÷ 5 = 1089   6534 ÷ 6 = 1089   7623 ÷ 7 = 1089
8712 ÷ 8 = 1089   9801 ÷ 9 = 1089

page 43
Percentages

I. blue 20%   yellow 80%   **2.** blue 25%   yellow 75%
3. blue 46%   yellow 54%   **4.** blue 10%   yellow 90%
5. blue 70%   yellow 30%   **6.** blue 54%   yellow 46%
7. blue 89%   yellow 11%   **8.** blue 12%   yellow 88%
9. blue 58%   yellow 42%

10. 10% of £60 = £6   **II.** 10% of £120 = £12   **I2.** 10% of £560 = £56
13. 10% of £380 = £38   **I4.** 10% of £990 = £99   **I5.** 10% of £1070 = £107
I6. 10% of £2200 = £220 **I7.** 10% of £6010 = £601 **I8.** 10% of £10 = £1

Number Textbook 2

@

10. 15% of £60 = £9
11. 15% of £120 = £18
12. 15% of £560 = £84
13. 15% of £380 = £57
14. 15% of £990 = £148·50
15. 15% of £1070 = £160·50
16. 15% of £2200 = £330
17. 15% of £6010 = £901·50
18. 15% of £10 = £1·50

Percentages

1. 20% of 140 = 28   28 voted 'yes'
2. 30% of 280 = 84   84 voted 'yes'
3. 40% of 190 = 76   76 voted 'yes'
4. 50% of 250 = 125   125 voted 'yes'
5. 10% of 360 = 36   36 voted 'yes'
6. 30% of 180 = 54   54 voted 'yes'
7. 20% of 340 = 68   68 voted 'yes'
8. 40% of 170 = 68   68 voted 'yes'
9. 60% of 220 = 132   132 voted 'yes'

10. 80% of 200 = 160
11. 30% of 120 = 36
12. 40% of 40 = 16
13. 20% of 350 = 70
14. 50% of 36 = 18
15. 10% of 400 = 40
16. 30% of 300 = 90
17. 70% of 200 = 140
18. 20% of 150 = 30
19. 90% of 500 = 450
20. 60% of 600 = 360
21. 40% of 250 = 100

Percentages

1. 50% of 160 = 80 children
2. 40% of 300 = 120 children
3. 20% of 180 = 36 children
4. 40% of 440 = 176 children
5. 10% of 140 = 14 children
6. 20% of 240 = 48 children
7. 25% of 400 = 100 children
8. 75% of 200 = 150 children

9. 30% of £30 = £9   £30 − £9 = £21
10. 20% of £60 = £12   £60 − £12 = £48
11. 40% of £20 = £8   £20 − £8 = £12
12. 25% of £40 = £10   £40 − £10 = £30
13. 75% of £80 = £60   £80 − £60 = £20
14. 60% of £50 = £30   £50 − £30 = £20
15. 25% of £70 = £17·50   £70 − £17·50 = £52·50
16. 75% of £30 = £22·50   £30 − £22·50 = £7·50

Number Textbook 2

Percentages

I. 12% of 350 = 42 children

3. 24% of 350 = 84 children

5. 16% of 450 = 72 children

7. 28% of 450 = 126 children

9. 18% of 350 = 63 children

2. 20% of 450 = 90 children

4. 20% of 350 = 70 children

6. 14% of 450 = 63 children

8. 26% of 350 = 91 children

Explore

Answers will vary.

Fractions, decimals and percentages

I–14

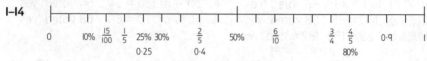

ℯ

10% $\frac{15}{100}$ $\frac{1}{5}$ $0{\cdot}25 = 25\%$ 30% $\frac{2}{5} = 0{\cdot}4$ 50% $\frac{6}{10}$ $\frac{3}{4}$

$\frac{4}{5} = 80\%$ $0{\cdot}9$

15. $40\% = \frac{2}{5} = 0{\cdot}4$ 16. $30\% = \frac{3}{10} = 0{\cdot}3$ 17. $20\% = \frac{1}{5} = 0{\cdot}2$

18. $5\% = \frac{1}{20} = 0{\cdot}05$ 19. $10\% = \frac{1}{10} = 0{\cdot}1$ 20. $80\% = \frac{4}{5} = 0{\cdot}8$

21. $75\% = \frac{3}{4} = 0{\cdot}75$ 22. $2\% = \frac{1}{50} = 0{\cdot}02$ 23. $35\% = \frac{7}{20} = 0{\cdot}35$

24. $45\% = \frac{9}{20} = 0{\cdot}45$ 25. $7\% = \frac{7}{100} = 0{\cdot}07$ 26. $60\% = \frac{3}{5} = 0{\cdot}6$

Fractions, decimals and percentages

I. $25\% = \frac{1}{4}$ 2. $0{\cdot}3 = \frac{3}{10}$ 3. $\frac{12}{100} = 12\%$ 4. $\frac{73}{100} = 0{\cdot}73$

5. $\frac{2}{10} = 20\%$ 6. $54\% = \frac{54}{100}$ 7. $\frac{14}{100} = 0{\cdot}14$ 8. $\frac{1}{5} = 20\%$

9. $0{\cdot}18 = \frac{18}{100}$ 10. $50\% = \frac{5}{10}$ II. $75\% > 0{\cdot}68$ 12. $0{\cdot}71 > \frac{17}{100}$

13. $0{\cdot}36 = \frac{36}{100}$ 14. $85\% = 0{\cdot}85$ 15. $\frac{27}{100} < 30\%$ 16. $55\% > \frac{44}{100}$

17. $31\% > 0{\cdot}13$ 18. $21\% = \frac{21}{100}$ 19. $0{\cdot}43 < \frac{44}{100}$ 20. $8\% < \frac{80}{100}$

21. $0{\cdot}27, \frac{35}{100}, 50\%$ 22. $\frac{70}{100}, 71\%, 0{\cdot}75$ 23. $0{\cdot}33, 34\%, \frac{43}{100}$

24. $8\%, 0{\cdot}18, \frac{81}{100}$ 25. $0{\cdot}9, 91\%, \frac{99}{100}$ 26. $2\%, \frac{2}{10}, 0{\cdot}21$

27. $0{\cdot}2, 25\%, \frac{3}{10}$

Number Textbook 2

Fractions, decimals and percentages

1. $\frac{3}{4} = 0.75$ 2. $\frac{2}{5} = 0.4$ 3. $\frac{1}{8} = 0.125$

4. $\frac{3}{8} = 0.375$ 5. $\frac{7}{20} = 0.35$ 6. $\frac{4}{5} = 0.8$

7. $\frac{1}{5} = 0.2$ 8. $\frac{5}{8} = 0.625$ 9. $\frac{7}{8} = 0.875$

10. $\frac{6}{15} = 0.4$ 11. $\frac{9}{25} = 0.36$

12. $\frac{3}{8} < \frac{4}{10}$ 13. $\frac{3}{5} < \frac{17}{20}$ 14. $\frac{1}{4} < \frac{5}{16}$ 15. $\frac{2}{7} < \frac{30}{100}$

16. $\frac{37}{50} > \frac{2}{3}$ 17. $\frac{6}{7} > \frac{21}{25}$ 18. $\frac{4}{9} > \frac{5}{12}$

19. $\frac{1}{3}$ of 60 = 20   There are 20 children.   60% of 20 = 12

There are 12 girls and 8 boys.

20. $\frac{3}{8}$ of 72 = 27 red   25% of 72 = 18 blue $\frac{1}{3}$ of 72 = 24 green

72 − (27 + 18 + 24) = 3   He has 3 silver marbles.

21. $\frac{1}{6}$ of 30 = 5 won   20% of 30 = 6 drawn   30 − (5 + 6) = 19 lost

22. $\frac{1}{7}$ of £35 = £5 for milkshakes   40% of £35 = £14 for ice creams

£35 − (£5 + £14) = £16 for burgers

Proportion

1. $\frac{6}{16} = \frac{3}{8}$ red $\frac{5}{8}$ white   2. $\frac{4}{16} = \frac{1}{4}$ red $\frac{3}{4}$ white

3. $\frac{14}{25}$ red $\frac{11}{25}$ white   4. $\frac{4}{12} = \frac{1}{3}$ red $\frac{2}{3}$ white

5. $\frac{8}{36} = \frac{2}{9}$ red $\frac{7}{9}$ white   6. $\frac{6}{18} = \frac{1}{3}$ red $\frac{2}{3}$ white

7. $\frac{8}{16} = \frac{1}{2}$ red $\frac{1}{2}$ white   8. $\frac{10}{15} = \frac{2}{3}$ red $\frac{1}{3}$ white

9. red = $\frac{4}{16} = \frac{1}{4}$ 10. red = $\frac{5}{12}$ 11. red = $\frac{5}{20} = \frac{1}{4}$ 12. red = $\frac{6}{18} = \frac{1}{3}$

blue = $\frac{6}{16} = \frac{3}{8}$ blue = $\frac{3}{12} = \frac{1}{4}$ blue = $\frac{8}{20} = \frac{2}{5}$ blue = $\frac{3}{18} = \frac{1}{6}$

yellow = $\frac{6}{16} = \frac{3}{8}$ yellow = $\frac{4}{12} = \frac{1}{3}$ yellow = $\frac{7}{20}$ yellow = $\frac{9}{18} = \frac{1}{2}$

13. red = $\frac{8}{12} = \frac{2}{3}$ 14. red = $\frac{10}{30} = \frac{1}{3}$ 15. red = $\frac{6}{18} = \frac{1}{3}$ 16. red = $\frac{5}{24}$

blue = $\frac{3}{12} = \frac{1}{4}$ blue = $\frac{12}{30} = \frac{2}{5}$ blue = $\frac{8}{18} = \frac{4}{9}$ blue = $\frac{8}{24} = \frac{1}{3}$

yellow = $\frac{1}{12}$ yellow = $\frac{8}{30} = \frac{4}{15}$ yellow = $\frac{4}{18} = \frac{2}{9}$ yellow = $\frac{11}{24}$

Number Textbook 2

Proportion

1. $\frac{6}{24} = \frac{1}{4}$ of the day asleep $\frac{3}{4}$ of the day awake

2. $\frac{8}{24} = \frac{1}{3}$ of the day asleep $\frac{2}{3}$ of the day awake

3. $\frac{10}{24} = \frac{5}{12}$ of the day asleep $\frac{7}{12}$ of the day awake

4. $\frac{12}{24} = \frac{1}{2}$ of the day asleep $\frac{1}{2}$ of the day awake

5. $\frac{9}{24} = \frac{3}{8}$ of the day asleep $\frac{5}{8}$ of the day awake

6. $\frac{11}{24}$ of the day asleep $\frac{13}{24}$ of the day awake

7. $\frac{7}{24}$ of the day asleep $\frac{17}{24}$ of the day awake

8. $\frac{15}{24} = \frac{5}{8}$ of the day asleep $\frac{3}{8}$ of the day awake

9. $\frac{15}{60} = \frac{1}{4}$ are not chocolates $\frac{1}{3}$ of 15 = 5   There are 5 toffees.

10. $\frac{2}{3}$ of the choir = 18 $(18 \div 2) \times 3 = 27$ children in the choir

11. $\frac{3}{5}$ of litter = 6 $5 \times 2 = 10$ kittens in the litter

12. I hour news, $\frac{1}{2}$ hour of adverts $6 - 1\frac{1}{2} = 4\frac{1}{2}$ hours not news or adverts

Proportion

1. $\frac{20}{30} = \frac{2}{3}$ of June is sunny   2. $\frac{6}{30} = \frac{1}{5}$ of June is rainy

3. $\frac{12}{30} = \frac{2}{5}$ of June is windy   4. $\frac{4}{30} = \frac{2}{15}$ of June is cloudy

5. $\frac{8}{30} = \frac{4}{15}$ of June is weekends   6. $\frac{5}{30} = \frac{1}{6}$ of June is Mondays

7. $\frac{9}{30} = \frac{3}{10}$ of June is half-term

8. 4 red   8 yellow   4 blue   6 green   2 white

9. 2 blue   8 red   5 green   3 yellow   2 white

10. 4 yellow   2 white   8 red   6 blue   12 green

11. 7 green   4 white   2 red   7 blue   8 yellow

12. 6 blue   3 green   9 yellow   12 white   5 red   1 black

Ratio and proportion

1. 3:5   2. 3:5   3. 3:4   4. 4:5   5. 1:4

6. 1:2   7. 1:1   8. 2:5   9. 1:2   10. 2:3

11. 7:5   12. 2:1   13. 3:2   14. 6:5   15. 3:8

❷

1. $\frac{5}{8}$		2. $\frac{5}{8}$		3. $\frac{4}{7}$		4. $\frac{5}{9}$		5. $\frac{4}{5}$	
6. $\frac{2}{3}$		7. $\frac{1}{2}$		8. $\frac{5}{7}$		9. $\frac{2}{3}$		10. $\frac{3}{5}$	
11. $\frac{5}{12}$		12. $\frac{1}{3}$		13. $\frac{2}{5}$		14. $\frac{5}{11}$		15. $\frac{8}{11}$	

16. 17. 18.
19. 20. 21.
22. 23.
24. 25.

Ratio and proportion

1. 1:2   2. 8:7   3. 4:1   4. 4:11   5. 1:3   6. 11:20   7. 12:19

❷

1. $\frac{1}{3}$ of the days were wet   2. $\frac{8}{15}$ of the days were wet
3. $\frac{4}{5}$ of the days were wet   4. $\frac{4}{15}$ of the days were wet
5. $\frac{1}{4}$ of the days were wet   6. $\frac{11}{31}$ of the days were wet
7. $\frac{12}{31}$ of the days were wet

8. 2:1 $\frac{1}{3}$ of 30 = 10 chocolate biscuits 9. 3:1 $\frac{1}{4}$ of 20 = 5 chocolate biscuits
10. 1:4 $\frac{4}{5}$ of 25 = 20 chocolate biscuits 11. 2:3 $\frac{3}{5}$ of 20 = 12 chocolate biscuits
12. 2:5 $\frac{5}{7}$ of 21 = 15 chocolate biscuits 13. 5:3 $\frac{3}{8}$ of 24 = 9 chocolate biscuits

---

Ratio and proportion

1. $20 \div 4 = 5$ $5 \times 3 = 15$ roses   2. $6 \div 3 = 2$ 2 lilies
3. $40 \div 4 = 10$ $10 \times 3 = 30$ roses   4. $36 \div 4 = 9$ 9 lilies
5. $18 \times 3 = 54$ roses   6. $32 \div 4 = 8$ $8 \times 3 = 24$ roses

7. $\frac{5}{8}$ 8. $\frac{1}{6}$ 9. $\frac{5}{7}$ 10. $\frac{3}{7}$ 11. $\frac{7}{9}$

Explore

Answers will vary.

Number Textbook 2

1. $19 + 36 + 45 + 23 + 21 = 144$
2. $9 + 8 + 2·3 + 7 + 6·5 = 32·8$
3. $7 + 7·5 + 8·4 + 10 + 2·3 = 35·2$
4. $12 + 2·8 + 1·9 + 4·7 + 13 = 34·4$
5. $11 + 9 + 1·7 + 3·1 + 4 = 28·8$
6. $1·9 + 7 + 9·8 + 20 + 3·7 = 42·4$
7. $6·9 + 13·2 + 5·7 + 1·5 + 19 = 46·3$
8. $1·7 + 10·2 + 7·1 + 17 + 12 = 48$
9. $3·9 + 9·7 + 5·7 + 5·4 + 9·4 = 34·1$
10. $1·9 + 17 + 6·8 + 3·4 + 13·5 = 42·6$

11. correct
12. incorrect $6·2 - 4·6 = 1·6$
13. incorrect $8·5 - 2·7 = 5·8$
14. correct
15. incorrect $4·3 - 3·6 = 0·7$
16. correct

Subtracting

1. correct 2. correct 3. correct 4. correct 5. correct 6. correct

Explore

Some examples are:

$456 - 321 = 135$ $654 - 321 = 333$ $765 - 432 = 333$ $765 - 123 = 642$

The answers can have:

1 all digits the same e.g. 333, 444
2 consecutive odd digits e.g. 135, 753
3 consecutive even digits e.g. 642, 246

Adding and subtracting

1. $3·1 + 2·7 + 2·8 + 5·2 + 2·3 + 1·9 = 18$ minutes $20 - 18 = 2$ minutes left
2. $88 + 56 + 79 + 46 + 43 + 64 = 376$ 376p = £3·76
   £5 - £3·76 = £1.24 so Sam gets incorrect change
3. 5 eggs × 15 = 75 eggs per week   1 month ≈ 4 weeks
   March to July = 5 months ≈ 20 weeks   75 eggs × 20 = 1500 eggs
   12p × 1500 = 18 000p = £180
4. corrected answers $7·6 - 3·75 = 3·85$ $5 - 1·36 = 3·64$
   $8·2 - 5·38 = 2·82$ $6·46 - 4·64 = 1·82$
5. 1035 ÷ 45 = 23 flowers per row
   after one month 1035 - 990 = 45 flowers have died
   990 ÷ 45 = 22 flowers left per row
6. $15 + 17 + 25 + 13 + 16 + 22 + 19 + 8 + 23 + 19 + 21 + 12 = 210$ £210

Number Textbook 2

page 59

Checking results

1. 42·7 + 36·9 + 23·5 = 103·1
3. 38·52 − 18·78 = 19·74
5. 412·7 − 286·8 = 125·9
7. 189·3 − 97·82 = 91·48
9. 587 − 479 = 108
11. 646·7 − 37·94 = 608·76
13. 101·11 − 87·8 = 13·31

2. 54 + 76 + 293 = 423
4. 36 + 28 +73 + 45 = 182
6. 318 + 79 + 162 + 39 = 598
8. 41·79 + 6·81 + 3·17 + 59·3 = 111·07
10. 718 + 3·65 + 396·4 = 1118·05
12. 1·29 + 812·3 + 723·41 = 1537

Explore

Adding any number to 8 × its digital root ensures that the answer is a multiple of 9. All multiples of 9 have a digital root of 9.

---

page 60

Patterns

	Multiples	Units digits
×2	2, 4, 6, 8, 10, 12, 14, 16, 18, 20 …	2, 4, 6, 8, 0, 2, 4, 6, 8, 0 …
×3	3, 6, 9, 12, 15, 18, 21, 24, 27, 30 …	3, 6, 9, 2, 5, 8, 1, 4, 7, 0 …
×4	4, 8, 12, 16, 20, 24, 28, 32, 36, 40 …	4, 8, 2, 6, 0, 4, 8, 2, 6, 0 …
×5	5, 10, 15, 20, 25, 30, 35, 40, 45, 50 …	5, 0, 5, 0, 5, 0, 5, 0, 5, 0, 5 …
×6	6, 12, 18, 24, 30, 36, 42, 48, 54, 60 …	6, 2, 8, 4, 0, 6, 2, 8, 4, 0 …
×7	7, 14, 21, 28, 35, 42, 49, 56, 63, 70 …	7, 4, 1, 8, 5, 2, 9, 6, 3, 0 …
×8	8, 16, 24, 32, 40, 48, 56, 64, 72, 80 …	8, 6, 4, 2, 0, 8, 6, 4, 2 …
×9	9, 18, 27, 36, 45, 54, 63, 72, 81, 90 …	9, 8, 7, 6, 5, 4, 3, 2, 1, 0 …

×2: the pattern uses the digits 2, 4, 6, 8, 0 …
×3: the pattern uses all the digits 0 to 9.
×4: the pattern uses the digits 4, 8, 2, 6, 0 …
×5: the pattern only uses two digits, 0 and 5.
×6: the pattern uses the digits 6, 2, 8, 4, 0, …
×7: the pattern uses all the digits 0 to 9.
×8: the pattern uses the digits 8, 6, 4, 2, 0, …
×9: the pattern uses all the digits 0 to 9 in order, 9, 8, 7, 6, 5, 4, 3, 2, 1, 0, …

The patterns of the multiples of even numbers 2, 4, 6, 8 are similar.

The patterns use the same digits (0 and the even digits) in different orders.

Number Textbook 2

Explore

Answers will vary. They may include

<u>addition only</u> $1 + 2 + 6 = 9$ <u>subtraction only</u> $12 - 3 = 9$
                 $1 + 3 + 5 = 9$ $13 - 4 = 9$
                 $2 + 2 + 5 = 9$ $14 - 5 = 9$
                 $2 + 3 + 4 = 9$

<u>addition and</u> $4 + 6 - 1 = 9$ <u>multiplication</u> $3 \times (4 - 1) = 9$
<u>subtraction</u> $5 + 7 - 3 = 9$ $3 \times (5 - 2) = 9$
                 $6 + 7 - 4 = 9$ <u>division</u> $36 \div 4 = 9$
                                                      $27 \div 3 = 9$

Patterns

1. $4 \cdot 63 - 1 \cdot 95 = 2 \cdot 68$ 2. $5 \cdot 25 - 2 \cdot 78 = 2 \cdot 47$ 3. $9 \cdot 26 - 3 \cdot 67 = 5 \cdot 59$
4. $3 \cdot 62 + 2 \cdot 87 = 6 \cdot 49$ 5. $8 \cdot 77 - 4 \cdot 73 = 4 \cdot 04$ 6. $7 \cdot 38 + 1 \cdot 75 = 9 \cdot 13$
7. $9 \cdot 86 - 6 \cdot 79 = 3 \cdot 07$ 8. $5 \cdot 38 + 4 \cdot 62 = 10$ 9. $6 \cdot 34 - 5 \cdot 91 = 0 \cdot 43$
10. $7 \cdot 63 + 3 \cdot 81 = 11 \cdot 44$ 11. $5 \cdot 78 - 4 \cdot 72 = 1 \cdot 06$ OR $5 \cdot 88 - 4 \cdot 72 = 1 \cdot 16$ etc
12. $3 \cdot 78 + 2 \cdot 73 = 6 \cdot 51$

Explore

1, 3, 4, 7, 11, 18, 29, 47, 76, 123, 199, 322, 521, 843
2, 6, 8, 14, 22, 36, 58, 94, 152, 246, 398, 644, 1042, 1686
5, 9, 14, 23, 37, 60, 97, 157, 254, 411, 665, 1076, 1741, 2817
2, 4, 6, 10, 16, 26, 42, 68, 110, 178, 288, 466, 754, 1220,
5, 8, 13, 21, 34, 55, 89, 144, 233, 377, 610, 987, 1597, 2584

If a sequence starts odd, odd, the pattern of the terms is odd, odd, even, odd, odd, even, ...
This is because O + O = E, then O + E = O.

If a sequence starts even, even, all the terms are even.
This is because E + E = E.

If a sequence starts odd, even, the pattern of the terms becomes odd, odd, even, odd, odd, even from the third term.
This is because O + E = O, E + O = O, O + O = O.
Then it follows the first type of pattern.

Number Textbook 2

Square numbers

1. $2 \times 2 = 4$ 2. $10 \times 10 = 100$ 3. $9 \times 9 = 81$ 4. $8 \times 8 = 64$
5. $3 \times 3 = 9$ 6. $4 \times 4 = 16$ 7. $5 \times 5 = 25$ 8. $6 \times 6 = 36$
9. $7 \times 7 = 49$

10. $20 \times 20 = 400$ 11. $30 \times 30 = 900$ 12. $40 \times 40 = 1600$
13. $50 \times 50 = 2500$ 14. $15 \times 15 = 225$

15. $21^2 = 441$ 16. $32^2 = 1024$ 17. $17^2 = 289$ 18. $19^2 = 361$
19. $26^2 = 676$ 20. $52^2 = 2704$ 21. $44^2 = 1936$ 22. $16^2 = 256$
23. $29^2 = 841$ 24. $25^2 = 625$ 25. $13^2 = 169$

Square numbers

number	1	2	3	4	5	6	7	8	9	10	11	12
square	1	4	9	16	25	36	49	64	81	100	121	144

20	30	40	50	60	70	80	90	100	200	300	400
400	900	1600	2500	3600	4900	6400	8100	10000	40000	90000	160000

1. $41^2 = 1681$ 2. $9 \cdot 5^2 = 90 \cdot 25$ 3. $21^2 = 441$ 4. $89^2 = 7921$
5. $6 \cdot 25^2 = 39 \cdot 0625$ 6. $15^2 = 225$ 7. $17^2 = 289$ 8. $101^2 = 10201$
9. $500^2 = 250\,000$ 10. $69^2 = 4761$ 11. $25^2 = 625$ 12. $16^2 = 256$
13. $32^2 = 1024$ 14. $74^2 = 5476$ 15. $55^2 = 3025$

16. $15 \times 16 = 240$ 17. $13 \times 12 = 156$ 18. $49 \times 50 = 2450$
19. $12 \times 11 = 132$ 20. $14 \times 15 = 210$ 21. $50 \times 51 = 2550$

ⓔ
Answers will vary.

Square numbers

1. 484 cm^2 $22^2 = 484$ side = 22 cm
2. 2601 cm^2 $51^2 = 2601$ side = 51 cm
3. 2025 cm^2 $45^2 = 2025$ side = 45 cm
4. $20 \cdot 25 \text{ m}^2$ $4 \cdot 5^2 = 20 \cdot 25$ side = 4·5 m

Number Textbook 2

5.	1·44 m²		$1·2^2 = 1·44$	side = 1·2 m
6.	12·25 cm²	$3·5^2 = 12·25$	side = 3·5 cm	
7.	196 cm²		$14^2 = 196$	side = 14 cm
8.	289 cm²		$172^2 = 289$	side = 17 cm
9.	0·25 m²		$0·5^2 = 0·25$	side = 0·5 m
10.	841 cm²		$29^2 = 841$	side = 29 cm
11.	1296 cm²	$36^2 = 1296$	side = 36 cm	

Explore

$111^2 = 12321$

$1111^2 = 1234321$

$11111^2 = 123454321$

$111111^2 = 12345654321$

The pattern continues.

Sequences

1.	7	11	15	19	23	27	31	35	add 4 each time
2.	3	5·5	8	10·5	13	15·5	18	20·5	add 2·5 each time
3.	3	10	17	24	31	38	45	52	add 7 each time
4.	$\frac{1}{2}$,	1,	$1\frac{1}{2}$,	2,	$2\frac{1}{2}$,	3,	$3\frac{1}{2}$,	4	add $\frac{1}{2}$ each time
5.	9	9·25	9·5	9·75	10	10·25	10·5	10·75	add 0·25 each time
6.	260	271	282	293	304	315	326	337	add 11 each time
7.	11·6	12·2	12·8	13·4	14·0	14·6	15·2	15·8	add 0·6 each time
8.	38·3	38·6	38·9	39·2	39·5	39·8	40·1	40·4	add 0·3 each time

1, 3, 6, 10, 15, 21, 28, 36, 45, 55, 66, 78, 91, 105, 120, 136, 153, 171, 190, 210
difference is ascending number sequence 1, 2, 3, 4 etc.

1, 3, 6, 10, 15, 21, 28, 36, 45, 55, 66, 78, 91, 105, 120, 136, 153, 171, 190, 210

Find the next term in the sequence by adding the number of the position in the sequence to the last term in the sequence.

@

4 9 16 25 36 49 64 81 100 121 144 169 196 225 256 289 324 361 400
This is the sequence of square numbers.

Number Textbook 2

Sequences

1. $7, 7\frac{1}{2}, 8, 8\frac{1}{2}, 9, 9\frac{1}{2}, 10, 10\frac{1}{2}, 11$
   Add $\frac{1}{2}$ each time.

2. $27, 25, 23, 21, 19, 17, 15, 13$
   Subtract 2 each time.

3. $0.7, 1.4, 2.1, 2.8, 3.5, 4.2, 4.9, 5.6$
   Add 0.7 each time.

4. $2\frac{3}{8}, 2\frac{5}{8}, 2\frac{7}{8}, 3\frac{1}{8}, 3\frac{3}{8}, 3\frac{5}{8}, 3\frac{7}{8}, 4\frac{1}{8}$
   Add $\frac{2}{8}$ ($\frac{1}{4}$) each time.

5. $1020, 1115, 1210, 1305, 1400, 1495, 1590, 1685$
   Add 95 each time.

6. $0.15, 0.8, 1.45, 2.1, 2.75, 3.4, 4.05, 4.7$ Add 0.65 each time.

7. $19\frac{5}{7}, 18\frac{4}{7}, 17\frac{3}{7}, 16\frac{2}{7}, 15\frac{1}{7}, 14, 12\frac{6}{7}, 11\frac{5}{7}$ Subtract $1\frac{1}{7}$ each time.

8. $11.7, 11.4, 11.1, 10.8, 10.5, 10.2, 9.9, 9.6$ Subtract 0.3 each time.

Explore

13, 21, 34, 55, 89, 144, 233, 377, 610, 987, 1597, 2584, 4181, 6765, 10 946, 17 711, 28 657, 46 368, 75 025, 121 393

Sequences

Answers will vary.

×2 table	×3 table	×4 table
$1 \times 2 = 2 \rightarrow 2$	$1 \times 3 = 3 \rightarrow 3$	$1 \times 4 = 4 \rightarrow 4$
$2 \times 2 = 4 \rightarrow 4$	$2 \times 3 = 6 \rightarrow 6$	$2 \times 4 = 8 \rightarrow 8$
$3 \times 2 = 6 \rightarrow 6$	$3 \times 3 = 9 \rightarrow 9$	$3 \times 4 = 12 \rightarrow 3$
$4 \times 2 = 8 \rightarrow 8$	$4 \times 3 = 12 \rightarrow 3$	$4 \times 4 = 16 \rightarrow 7$
$5 \times 2 = 10 \rightarrow 1$	$5 \times 3 = 15 \rightarrow 6$	$5 \times 4 = 20 \rightarrow 2$
$6 \times 2 = 12 \rightarrow 3$	$6 \times 3 = 18 \rightarrow 9$	$6 \times 4 = 24 \rightarrow 6$
$7 \times 2 = 14 \rightarrow 5$	$7 \times 3 = 21 \rightarrow 3$	$7 \times 4 = 28 \rightarrow 10 \rightarrow 1$
$8 \times 2 = 16 \rightarrow 7$	$8 \times 3 = 24 \rightarrow 6$	$8 \times 4 = 32 \rightarrow 5$
$9 \times 2 = 18 \rightarrow 9$	$9 \times 3 = 27 \rightarrow 9$	$9 \times 4 = 36 \rightarrow 9$
$10 \times 2 = 20 \rightarrow 2$	$10 \times 3 = 30 \rightarrow 3$	$10 \times 4 = 40 \rightarrow 4$

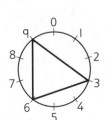

Number Textbook 2

page 67 cont ...

×5 table

$1 \times 5 = 5 \to 5$
$2 \times 5 = 10 \to 1$
$3 \times 5 = 15 \to 6$
$4 \times 5 = 20 \to 2$
$5 \times 5 = 25 \to 7$
$6 \times 5 = 30 \to 3$
$7 \times 5 = 35 \to 8$
$8 \times 5 = 40 \to 4$
$9 \times 5 = 45 \to 9$
$10 \times 5 = 50 \to 5$

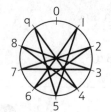

×6 table

$1 \times 6 = 6 \to 6$
$2 \times 6 = 12 \to 3$
$3 \times 6 = 18 \to 9$
$4 \times 6 = 24 \to 6$
$5 \times 6 = 30 \to 3$
$6 \times 6 = 36 \to 9$
$7 \times 6 = 42 \to 6$
$8 \times 6 = 48 \to 12 \to 3$
$9 \times 6 = 54 \to 9$
$10 \times 6 = 60 \to 6$

×7 table

$1 \times 7 = 7 \to 7$
$2 \times 7 = 14 \to 5$
$3 \times 7 = 21 \to 3$
$4 \times 7 = 28 \to 10 \to 1$
$5 \times 7 = 35 \to 8$
$6 \times 7 = 42 \to 6$
$7 \times 7 = 49 \to 13 \to 4$
$8 \times 7 = 56 \to 11 \to 2$
$9 \times 7 = 63 \to 9$
$10 \times 7 = 70 \to 7$

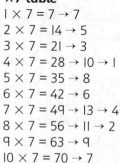
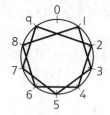

×8 table

$1 \times 8 = 8 \to 8$
$2 \times 8 = 16 \to 7$
$3 \times 8 = 24 \to 6$
$4 \times 8 = 32 \to 5$
$5 \times 8 = 40 \to 4$
$6 \times 8 = 48 \to 12 \to 3$
$7 \times 8 = 56 \to 11 \to 2$
$8 \times 8 = 64 \to 10 \to 1$
$9 \times 8 = 72 \to 9$
$10 \times 8 = 80 \to 8$

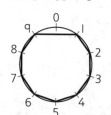

×9 table

$1 \times 9 = 9 \to 9$
$2 \times 9 = 18 \to 9$
$3 \times 9 = 27 \to 9$
$4 \times 9 = 36 \to 9$
$5 \times 9 = 45 \to 9$
$6 \times 9 = 54 \to 9$
$7 \times 9 = 63 \to 9$
$8 \times 9 = 72 \to 9$
$9 \times 9 = 81 \to 9$
$10 \times 9 = 90 \to 9$

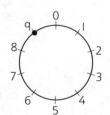

×10 table

$1 \times 10 = 10 \to 1$
$2 \times 10 = 20 \to 2$
$3 \times 10 = 30 \to 3$
$4 \times 10 = 40 \to 4$
$5 \times 10 = 50 \to 5$
$6 \times 10 = 60 \to 6$
$7 \times 10 = 70 \to 7$
$8 \times 10 = 80 \to 8$
$9 \times 10 = 90 \to 9$
$10 \times 10 = 100 \to 1$

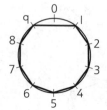

Number Textbook 2

 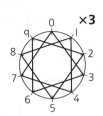  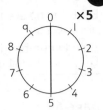

×2   ×3   ×4   ×5

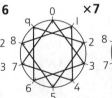 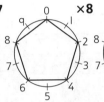 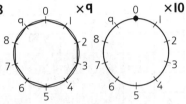

×6   ×7   ×8   ×9   ×10

Explore

| 8   27   64   125   196

$1 + 8 = 9$

$1 + 8 + 27 = 36$

$1 + 8 + 27 + 64 = 100$

i.e. $1^3 + 2^3 = 3^2$

$1^3 + 2^3 + 3^3 = 6^2$

$1^3 + 2^3 + 3^3 + 4^3 = 10^2$

The sum of the first n cubic numbers equals the nth triangular number.

---

page 68

Odd and even numbers

+	Even	Odd
Even	E	O
Odd	O	E

−	Even	Odd
Even	E	O
Odd	O	E

1. $12 \times 8 = 96$ even
3. $9 \times 12 = 108$ even
5. $6 \times 7 = 42$ even
7. $5 \times 12 = 60$ even

2. $7 \times 9 = 63$ odd
4. $3 \times 15 = 45$ odd
6. $8 \times 7 = 56$ even
8. $14 \times 4 = 56$ even

×	Even	Odd
Even	E	E
Odd	E	O

÷	Even	Odd
Even	E or O	E
Odd	–	O

Number Textbook 2

E ÷ E can be even, e.g. 12 ÷ 6 = 2, or odd, e.g. 12 ÷ 4 = 3 so answers E and O are possible.

An odd number divided by an even number will never give a whole number, so O ÷ E is impossible.

Odd and even numbers

×	1	2	3	4	5	6	7	8	9	10
1	1	2	3	4	5	6	7	8	9	10
2	2	4	6	8	10	12	14	16	18	20
3	3	6	9	12	15	18	21	24	27	30
4	4	8	12	16	20	24	28	32	36	40
5	5	10	15	20	25	30	35	40	45	50
6	6	12	18	24	30	36	42	48	54	60
7	7	14	21	28	35	42	49	56	63	70
8	8	16	24	32	40	48	56	64	72	80
9	9	18	27	36	45	54	63	72	81	90
10	10	20	30	40	50	60	70	80	90	100

Even numbers are shaded. There are 100 numbers on the grid, 75 even, 25 odd.

1. even	**2.** odd/even	**3.** odd/even	**4.** odd	**5.** odd/even
6. even	**7.** even	**8.** even	**9.** even	**10.** odd/even
11. odd/even	**12.** odd/even	**13.** odd/even	**14.** odd	

Odd and even numbers

1 = 1
3 + 5 = 8
7 + 9 + 11 = 27
13 + 15 + 17 + 19 = 64
21 + 23 + 25 + 27 + 29 = 125

The sum of the 10th row = 10^3 = 1000.

The sum of the nth row = n^3.

Explore

1	2	3	4	5	6	7	8	9	1
2	4	6	8	1	3	5	7	9	2
3	6	9	3	6	9	3	6	9	3
4	8	3	7	2	6	1	5	9	4
5	1	6	2	7	3	8	4	9	5
6	3	9	6	3	9	6	3	9	6
7	5	3	1	8	6	4	2	9	7
8	7	6	5	4	3	2	1	9	8
9	9	9	9	9	9	9	9	9	9
1	2	3	4	5	6	7	8	9	1

Notice:
- the 9th row and column are all 9s (the multiples of 9)
- symmetry about the leading diagonal (top L to bottom R)
- multiples of 3 and multiples of 6 are all 3s, 6s and 9s
- if the last 2 columns and last 2 rows are ignored, then the remaining 8×8 square has rotational symmetry about its centre.

---

page 71
Mixed problems

1. $\frac{1}{4}$ hour = 15 minutes = 60 seconds $\times$ 15 = 900 seconds

   $900 \div 10 = 90$ The pond holds 90 litres of water.

2. £34·60 $\times$ 2 = £69·20   £17·30 $\times$ 2 = £34·60   £69·20 + £34·60 = £103·80

   £103·80 for 1 night → £103·80 $\times$ 2 for 2 nights

   £135 + £207·60 = £342·60 → less than £500

3. possible combinations are:

6	6	1	1
6	5	2	1
6	4	3	1
6	4	2	2
6	3	3	2
5	5	3	1
5	5	2	2
5	4	4	1

Number Textbook 2

     5   4   3   2
     5   3   3   3
     4   4   3   3
     4   4   4   2

4. 22 days = 24 × 22 = 528 hours   0·6p × 528 = 316·8p ≈ £3·17
5. 24 visible faces   3 faces of each cube
6. bed 1 m × 2 m = 2 m²
   chest of drawers 1 m × 0·5 m = 0·5 m²
   wardrobe 0·75 × 0·5 = 0·375 m²
   bookcase 0·25 × 0·5 = 0·125 m²
   2 + 0·5 + 0·375 + 0·125 = 3 m²
   room 3 m × 4 m = 12 m²
   Proportion of floor space taken up by furniture = $\frac{3}{12}$ = $\frac{1}{4}$.
7. 1·5 seconds × 1 000 000 = 1 500 000 seconds
   1 500 000 seconds = 1 500 000 ÷ 60 = 25 000 minutes
   25 000 minutes = 25 000 ÷ 60 = 416 r 40 = 416 hours 40 minutes
   416 hours 40 minutes = 17 days 8 hours 40 minutes

---

page 72
Mixed problems

1. 500 sheets × 9 = 4500 sheets   12 weeks = 5 days × 12 = 60 days
   4500 ÷ 60 = 75 → 75 sheets used per day
2. Hilltop £3·25 × 27 = £87·75   Forest View is cheaper.
3. 8:00 a.m. to 10:00 p.m. = 14 hours = 60 minutes × 14 = 840 minutes
   840 ÷ 50 = 16·8 → Need 17 CDs
   50 ÷ 12 = $4\frac{1}{6}$ minutes
   Mean length of a track = 4 minutes 10 seconds.
4. £4·99 × 120 = £598·80   330 g × 120 = 39600 g = 39·6 kg
   Shop needs 4 boxes of 10 kg.   Cost = £9·99 × 4 = £39·96.
5. Most steps = 4 (number 77)
   Least steps = 1 (any number with a digit 1 e.g. 15, 91)
6. 1! = 1   2! = 2   3! = 6   4! = 24   5! = 120   6! = 720
   7! = 5040   8! = 40320   9! = 362 880   10! = 3 628 800
7. Answers will vary.

Shape, Data and Measures

page 3

Metres, centimetres, feet, inches

1a. 25 cm ≈ 10 inches

1b. 50 cm ≈ 20 inches = 1 foot 8 inches

2a. 30 cm ≈ 12 inches = 1 foot

2b. 45 cm ≈ 18 inches = 1 foot 6 inches

3a. 15 cm ≈ 6 inches

3b. 40 cm ≈ 16 inches = 1 foot 4 inches

4a. 35 cm ≈ 14 inches = 1 foot 2 inches

4b. 70 cm ≈ 28 inches = 2 feet 4 inches

5a. 20 cm ≈ 8 inches

5b. 55 cm ≈ 22 inches = 1 foot 10 inches

6a. 10 cm ≈ 4 inches

6b. 17·5 cm ≈ 7 inches

7a. 22·5 cm ≈ 9 inches

7b. 60 cm ≈ 24 inches = 2 feet

8a. 27·5 cm ≈ 11 inches

8b. 65 cm ≈ 26 inches = 2 feet 2 inches

@

1a. 250 mm	**1b.** 500 mm	**2a.** 300 mm	**2b.** 450 mm
3a. 150 mm	**3b.** 400 mm	**4a.** 350 mm	**4b.** 700 mm
5a. 200 mm	**5b.** 550 mm	**6a.** 100 mm	**6b.** 175 mm
7a. 225 mm	**7b.** 600 mm	**8a.** 275 mm	**8b.** 650 mm

9. 1 foot   **10.** 2·0 m   **11.** 60 feet   **12.** 3·3 m

---

page 4

Inches, feet, yards

1. 39 feet = 13 yards
13 yards ≈ 12 m

2. 30 feet = 10 yards
10 yards ≈ 9 m

3. 21 feet = 7 yards
7 yards ≈ 6 m

4. 54 feet = 18 yards
18 yards ≈ 17 m

5. 42 feet = 14 yards
14 yards ≈ 13 m

6. 27 feet = 9 yards
9 yards ≈ 8 m

7. 63 feet = 21 yards
21 yards ≈ 19 m

8. 18 feet = 6 yards
6 yards ≈ 5 m

@ **1.** 39 yards   **2.** 30 yards   **3.** 21 yards   **4.** 54 yards   **5.** 42 yards
6. 27 yards   **7.** 63 yards   **8.** 18 yards
9.–12. Answers will vary.

---

page 5

Miles and kilometres

1. 3990 m = 3·99 km   3·99 km is close to 4 km   3·99 km ≈ 2·5 miles
2. 2100 m = 2·1 km   2·1 km is close to 2 km   2·1 km ≈ 1·25 miles
3. 1070 m = 1·07 km   1·07 km is close to 1 km   1·07 km ≈ 0·7 miles
4. 1950 m = 1·95 km   1·95 km is close to 2 km   1·95 km ≈ 1·25 miles
5. 2980 m = 2·98 km   2·98 km is close to 3 km   2·98 km ≈ 1·9 miles

Shape, Data and Measures

page 5 cont ...

6. 3020 m = 3·02 km   3·02 km is close to 3 km   3·02 km ≈ 1·9 miles
7. 4010 m = 4·01 km   4·01 km is close to 4 km   4·01 km ≈ 2·5 miles
8. 1510 m = 1·51 km   1·51 km is close to 1·5 km   1·51 km ≈ 0·9 miles
9. 4500 m = 4·5 km   4·5 km ≈ 2·8 miles

ⓔ

1. 3990 m = 399 000 cm   399 000 cm ≈ 159 600 inches
2. 2100 m = 210 000 cm   210 000 cm ≈ 84 000 inches
3. 1070 m = 107 000 cm   107 000 cm ≈ 42 800 inches
4. 1950 m = 195 000 cm   195 000 cm ≈ 78 000 inches
5. 2980 m = 298 000 cm   298 000 cm ≈ 119 200 inches
6. 3020 m = 302 000 cm   302 000 cm ≈ 120 800 inches
7. 4010 m = 401 000 cm   401 000 cm ≈ 160 400 inches
8. 1510 m = 151 000 cm   151 000 cm ≈ 60 400 inches
9. 4500 m = 450 000 cm   450 000 cm ≈ 180 000 inches

10. train – metres
11. bug – millimetres
12. dresser – metres or centimetres
13. rucksack – centimetres
14. ear-rings – millimetres

---

page 6
Grams, kilograms, ounces, pounds

1. 3·5 kg = 3500 g
   3·5 kg ≈ 7 lb

2. 4·5 kg = 4500 g
   4·5 kg ≈ 9 lb

3. 1·25 kg = 1250 g
   1·25 kg ≈ $2\frac{1}{2}$ lb = 2 lb 8 oz

4. 6·25 kg = 6250 g
   6·25 kg ≈ $12\frac{1}{2}$ lb = 12 lb 8 oz

5. 3·75 kg = 3750 g
   3·75 kg ≈ $7\frac{1}{2}$ lb = 7 lb 8 oz

6. 5·75 kg = 5750 g
   5·75 kg ≈ $11\frac{1}{2}$ lb = 11 lb 8 oz

7. 2·125 kg = 2125 g
   2·125 kg ≈ $4\frac{1}{4}$ lb = 4 lb 4 oz

8. 5·375 kg = 5375 g
   5·375 kg ≈ $10\frac{3}{4}$ lb = 10 lb 12 oz

ⓔ 1. 14 lb   2. 18 lb   3. 5 lb   4. 25 lb   5. 15 lb   6. 23 lb   7. $8\frac{1}{2}$ lb   8. $21\frac{1}{2}$ lb

9. 1 kg   10. 200 g   11. 20 lb   12. 3 oz   13. 10 oz

Shape, Data and Measures

page 7

Pounds, ounces and kilograms

I. 2 lb ≈ 1 kg   **2.** 3 lb ≈ 1·5 kg   **3.** 8 oz ≈ 0·25 kg
4. 2 lb 4 oz ≈ 1·125 kg   **5.** 3 lb 8 oz ≈ 1·75 kg   **6.** 1 lb 12 oz ≈ 0·875 kg

10.–14. Answers will vary.

---

page 8

Pounds and ounces, tonnes

I. 33 lb ÷ 2·2 ≈ 15 kg   **2.** 39 lb ÷ 2·2 ≈ 17·7 kg
3. 44 lb ÷ 2·2 ≈ 20 kg   **4.** 26 lb ÷ 2·2 ≈ 11·8 kg
5. 32 lb ÷ 2·2 ≈ 14·5 kg   **6.** 47 lb ÷ 2·2 ≈ 21·4 kg
7. 46 lb ÷ 2·2 ≈ 20·9 kg   **8.** 34 lb ÷ 2·2 ≈ 15·5 kg
9. 51 lb ÷ 2·2 ≈ 23·2 kg

@ **6.**, **7.** and **9.** are too heavy.

7. 20 000 kg = 20 tonnes   **8.** 30 000 kg = 30 tonnes
9. 25 000 kg = 25 tonnes   **10.** 19 000 kg = 19 tonnes
II. 27 500 kg = 27·5 tonnes   **12.** 30 800 kg = 30·8 tonnes
13. 15 400 kg = 15·4 tonnes

---

page 9

Millilitres, litres, pints

I. 1·5 l = 1500 ml ≈ $2\frac{3}{4}$ pints   **2.** 3 l = 3000 ml ≈ $5\frac{1}{4}$ pints

3. 2·5 l = 2500 ml ≈ $4\frac{3}{8}$ pints   **4.** 2 l = 2000 ml ≈ $3\frac{1}{2}$ pints

5. 5·5 l = 5500 ml ≈ $9\frac{5}{8}$ pints   **6.** 4 l = 4000 ml ≈ 7 pints

7. 6 l = 6000 ml ≈ $10\frac{1}{2}$ pints   **8.** 4·5 l = 4500 ml ≈ $7\frac{7}{8}$ pints

9. 3·5 l = 3500 ml ≈ $6\frac{1}{8}$ pints   **10.** 1·25 l = 1250 ml ≈ $2\frac{3}{16}$ pints

II. 2·25 l = 2250 ml ≈ $3\frac{15}{16}$ pints

@ 150 cl   300 cl   250 cl   200 cl   550 cl   400 cl
   600 cl   450 cl   350 cl   125 cl   225 cl

12. 100 ml   **13.** 1 cl   **14.** $\frac{1}{2}$ pint   **15.** $\frac{1}{2}$ pint
16. 0·6 l   **17.** 1 pint

Shape, Data and Measures

Centilitres, litres, pints

1. 7 l = 700 cl   10 bottles   9 full, 25 cl left
2. 10 l = 1000 cl   14 bottles   13 full, 25 cl left
3. 15 l = 1500 cl   20 bottles   all full
4. 11·5 l = 1150 cl   16 bottles   15 full, 25 cl left
5. 25 l = 2500 cl   34 bottles   33 full, 25 cl left
6. 22·5 l = 2250 cl   30 bottles   all full
7. 17·5 l = 1750 cl   24 bottles   23 full, 25 cl left
8. 12·75 l = 1275 cl   17 bottles   all full
9. 18·5 l = 1850 cl   25 bottles   24 full, 50 cl left

☝ See answers above.

10. $2\frac{1}{2}$ pints ≈ 1·5 l   11. 4 pints ≈ 2·3 l   12. 2 pints ≈ 1·1 l
13. 3 pints ≈ 1·7 l   14. $1\frac{1}{2}$ pints ≈ 0·9 l   15. $4\frac{1}{2}$ pints ≈ 2·6 l
16. 6 pints ≈ 3·4 l

☝ 150 cl   230 cl   110 cl   170 cl   90 cl   260 cl   340 cl

---

Litres and gallons

1. 9 l ≈ 2 gallons   2. 45 l ≈ 10 gallons   3. 18 l ≈ 4 gallons
4. 36 l ≈ 8 gallons   5. 27 l ≈ 6 gallons   6. 22·5 l ≈ 5 gallons
7. 13·5 l ≈ 3 gallons

☝ 1. 16 pints   2. 80 pints   3. 32 pints   4. 64 pints
   5. 48 pints   6. 40 pints   7. 24 pints

8. 100 ÷ 25 = 4 gallons   9. 60 ÷ 30 = 2 gallons   10. 150 ÷ 30 = 5 gallons
   4 × 4·5 = 18   2 × 4·5 = 9   5 × 4·5 = 22·5
   4 gallons ≈ 18 litres   2 gallons ≈ 9 litres   5 gallons ≈ 22·5 litres

11. 70 ÷ 35 = 2 gallons   12. 120 ÷ 20 = 6 gallons   13. 75 ÷ 15 = 5 gallons
   2 × 4·5 = 9   6 × 4·5 = 27   5 × 4·5 = 22·5
   2 gallons ≈ 9 litres   6 gallons ≈ 27 litres   5 gallons ≈ 22·5 litres

14. 160 ÷ 40 = 4 gallons
   4 × 4·5 = 18
   4 gallons ≈ 18 litres

Shape, Data and Measures

page 12

Finding the area of rectangles

1. $5 \times 4 = 20$ Area = 20 m²
2. $16 \times 4 = 64$ Area = 64 m²
3. $2 \cdot 5 \times 10 = 25$ Area = 25 mm²
4. $60 \times 20 = 1200$ Area = 1200 mm²
5. $100 \times 31 = 3100$ Area = 3100 mm²
6. $20 \times 3 \cdot 5 = 70$ Area = 70 m²
7. $25 \times 17 = 425$ Area = 425 mm²

1. $500 \times 400 = 200\,000$ cm²
2. $1600 \times 400 = 640\,000$ cm²
3. $0 \cdot 25 \times 1 = 0 \cdot 25$ cm²
4. $6 \times 2 = 12$ cm²
5. $10 \times 3 \cdot 1 = 31$ cm²
6. $2000 \times 350 = 700\,000$ cm²
7. $2 \cdot 5 \times 1 \cdot 7 = 4 \cdot 25$ cm²

8. $2 \times 5 = 10$ $4 \times 3 = 12$ Area = 22 m²
9. $2 \times 7 = 14$ $6 \times 3 = 18$ Area = 32 m²
10. $4 \times 2 \cdot 5 = 10$ $3 \times 2 = 6$ Area = 16 m²

11. $15 \times 45 = 675$ $25 \times 15 = 375$ Area = 1050 cm²
12. $30 \times 25 = 750$ $20 \times 45 = 900$ Area = 1650 cm²
13. $65 \times 100 = 6500$ $15 \times 30 = 450$ Area = 6950 cm²

---

page 13

Finding the area of rectangles

1. $35 \times 80 = 2800$ $2 \times 2800 = 5600$ $25 \times 60 = 1500$ Area = 7100 cm²
2. $20 \times 30 = 600$ $2 \times 600 = 1200$ $40 \times 20 = 800$ Area = 2000 cm²
3. $25 \times 65 = 1625$ $2 \times 1625 = 3250$ $25 \times 55 = 1375$ Area = 4625 cm²
4. $85 \times 20 = 1700$ $2 \times 1700 = 3400$ $70 \times 50 = 3500$ Area = 6900 cm²
5. $100 \times 54 = 5400$ $70 \times 16 = 1120$ $10 \times 16 = 160$ Area = 6680 cm²
6. $50 \times 30 = 1500$ $18 \times 20 = 360$ $50 \times 15 = 750$ Area = 2610 cm²

1. Total area = $95 \times 80 = 7600$ cm²
   Area still to do: $7600 - 7100 = 500$ cm²
2. Total area = $80 \times 30 = 2400$ cm²
   Area still to do: $2400 - 2000 = 400$ cm²
3. Total area = $75 \times 65 = 4875$ cm²
   Area still to do: $4875 - 4625 = 250$ cm²
4. Total area = $85 \times 90 = 7650$ cm²
   Area still to do: $7650 - 6900 = 750$ cm²
5. Total area = $100 \times 70 = 7000$ cm²
   Area still to do: $7000 - 6680 = 320$ cm²
6. Total area = $50 \times 65 = 3250$ cm²
   Area still to do: $3250 - 2610 = 640$ cm²

Shape, Data and Measures

page 13 cont ...

7. $80 = 10 \times b$ $b = 8$ cm   **8.** $75 = 25 \times b$ $b = 3$ cm
9. $150 = 50 \times b$ $b = 3$ cm   **10.** $96 = b \times 12$ $b = 8$ cm
11. $100 = b \times 10$ $b = 10$ cm   **12.** $300 = b \times 15$ $b = 20$ cm

---

page 14
Surface area

1. top: $4 \times 2 = 8$ cm^2 side: $4 \times 1 = 4$ cm^2 front: $2 \times 1 = 2$ cm^2
Surface area $= 2 \times (8 + 4 + 2) = 2 \times 14 = 28$ cm^2

2. top: $8 \times 4 = 32$ cm^2 side: $8 \times 2 = 16$ cm^2 front: $4 \times 2 = 8$ cm^2
Surface area $= 2 \times (32 + 16 + 8) = 2 \times 56 = 112$ cm^2

3. top: $6 \times 5 = 30$ cm^2 side: $4 \times 6 = 24$ cm^2 front: $4 \times 5 = 20$ cm^2
Surface area $= 2 \times (30 + 24 + 20) = 2 \times 74 = 148$ cm^2

4. top: $7 \times 6 = 42$ cm^2 side: $7 \times 3 = 21$ cm^2 front: $6 \times 3 = 18$ cm^2
Surface area $= 2 \times (42 + 21 + 18) = 2 \times 81 = 162$ cm^2

5. top: $5 \times 8 = 40$ cm^2 side: $5 \times 9 = 45$ cm^2 front: $9 \times 8 = 72$ cm^2
Surface area $= 2 \times (40 + 45 + 72) = 2 \times 157 = 314$ cm^2

6. top: $11 \times 10 = 110$ cm^2 side: $11 \times 2 = 22$ cm^2 front: $10 \times 2 = 20$ cm^2
Surface area $= 2 \times (110 + 22 + 20) = 2 \times 152 = 304$ cm^2

7.
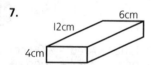

8.
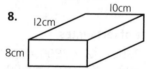

7. $24 + 72 + 48 = 144$ cm^2 $144 \times 2 = 288$ cm^2
8. $80 + 96 + 120 = 296$ cm^2 $296 \times 2 = 592$ cm^2

Explore

For rectangles with sides that are whole numbers of metres, possible perimeters are:

1 m × 240 m	p = 482 m	6 m × 40 m	p = 92 m
2 m × 120 m	p = 244 m	8 m × 30 m	p = 76 m
3 m × 80 m	p = 166 m	10 m × 24 m	p = 68 m
4 m × 60 m	p = 128 m	12 m × 20 m	p = 64 m
5 m × 48 m	p = 106 m	15 m × 16 m	p = 62 m

A small perimeter is obtained by making the L-shape as near as possible to a square.
An L-shape which is close to 15 m × 16 m (i.e. close to a square) is:

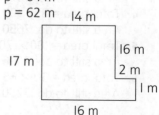

Shape, Data and Measures

page 14 cont ...

It has area $(14 \times 16) + (16 \times 1) = 240$ m². Its perimeter is $17 + 14 + 16 + 2 + 1 + 16 = 66$ m (assuming that all measures are in whole numbers of metres).

---

page 15

Finding the area of triangles

1. $\frac{1}{2}$ of $(6 \times 2) = 6$ Area = 6 cm²
2. $\frac{1}{2}$ of $(10 \times 20) = 100$ Area = 100 mm²
3. $\frac{1}{2}$ of $(15 \times 5) = 37 \cdot 5$ Area = 37·5 cm²
4. $\frac{1}{2}$ of $(14 \times 14) = 98$ Area = 98 mm²
5. $\frac{1}{2}$ of $(16 \times 9) = 72$ Area = 72 m²
6. $\frac{1}{2}$ of $(120 \times 50) = 3000$ Area = 3000 mm²
7. $\frac{1}{2}$ of $(12 \times 19) = 114$ Area = 114 cm²
8. $\frac{1}{2}$ of $(25 \times 9) = 112 \cdot 5$ Area = 112·5 m²

Explore

The rectangles which contain the right-angled triangles have an area of $2 \times 24 = 48$ cm². Possibilities are: 1 cm × 48 cm, 2 cm × 24 cm, 3 cm × 16 cm, 4 cm × 12 cm, 6 cm × 8 cm. These are the two short sides for each triangle. The triangle with short sides 6 cm and 8 cm has a longest side of 10 cm.

---

page 16

Finding the area of triangles

1. $\frac{1}{2}$ of $(7 \times 5) = 17\frac{1}{2}$ Area = $17\frac{1}{2}$ cm²
2. $\frac{1}{2}$ of $(12 \times 6) = 36$ Area = 36 cm²
3. $\frac{1}{2}$ of $(180 \times 100) = 9000$ Area = 9000 mm²
4. $\frac{1}{2}$ of $(9 \times 18) = 81$ Area = 81 cm²
5. $\frac{1}{2}$ of $(20 \times 12) = 120$ Area = 120 m²
6. $\frac{1}{2}$ of $(16 \times 20) = 160$ Area = 160 cm²
7. $\frac{1}{2}$ of $(25 \times 12) = 150$ Area = 150 cm²
8. $\frac{1}{2}$ of $(35 \times 8) = 140$ Area = 140 cm²
9. $\frac{1}{2}$ of $(18 \times 11) = 99$ Area = 99 m²
10. $\frac{1}{2}$ of $(16 \times 8) = 64$ Area = 64 m²

❷ Doubling the lengths increases the area by a scale factor of 4.

Shape, Data and Measures

11. $\frac{1}{2}$ of $(3 \times 5) = 7\frac{1}{2}$ Area $= 7\frac{1}{2}$ cm²

12. $\frac{1}{2}$ of $(6 \times 2) = 6$ Area $= 6$ cm²

13. $\frac{1}{2}$ of $(12 \times 9) = 54$ Area $= 54$ cm²

14. $\frac{1}{2}$ of $(24 \times 11) = 132$ Area $= 132$ cm²

15. $\frac{1}{2}$ of $(15 \times 6) = 45$ Area $= 45$ cm²

16. $\frac{1}{2}$ of $(17 \times 4) = 34$ Area $= 34$ cm²

17. $\frac{1}{2}$ of $(22 \times 9) = 99$ Area $= 99$ cm²

page 17

Area M5

Finding the area of triangles

1. $66 = L \times 6$ $66 \div 6 = L$ $L = 11$ cm
2. $80 = L \times 8$ $80 \div 8 = L$ $L = 10$ cm
3. $3000 = L \times 30$ $3000 \div 30 = L$ $L = 100$ mm
4. $128 = L \times 16$ $128 \div 16 = L$ $L = 8$ cm
5. $2000 = L \times 40$ $2000 \div 40 = L$ $L = 50$ mm
6. $54 = L \times 9$ $54 \div 9 = L$ $L = 6$ cm
7. $196 = L \times 14$ $196 \div 14 = L$ $L = 14$ cm
8. $5000 = L \times 50$ $5000 \div 50 = L$ $L = 100$ mm
9. $240 = L \times 12$ $240 \div 12 = L$ $L = 20$ cm

Explore

area of triangle 9 cm²   area of rectangle 18 cm²
The area of any triangle is always half of the surrounding rectangle.

page 18

Perimeter M6

Perimeter of rectangles

1. $(10 + 32) \times 2 = 84$ Perimeter $= 84$ m
2. $(12 + 44) \times 2 = 112$ Perimeter $= 112$ m
3. $(10 + 47) \times 2 = 114$ Perimeter $= 114$ yards
4. $(16 + 21) \times 2 = 74$ Perimeter $= 74$ yards
5. $(27 + 15) \times 2 = 84$ Perimeter $= 84$ m

page 18 cont ...

6. $(14 + 9) \times 2 = 46$ Perimeter $= 46$ yards
7. $(19 + 8) \times 2 = 54$ Perimeter $= 54$ m

Shape, Data and Measures

8. $(31 + 22) \times 2 = 106$ Perimeter = 106 yards
9. $(62 + 56) \times 2 = 236$ Perimeter = 236 feet
10. $(11 + 17) \times 2 = 56$ Perimeter = 56 m

e
$10 \times 32 = 320 \text{ m}^2$ $12 \times 44 = 528 \text{ m}^2$
$10 \times 47 = 470$ square yards $16 \times 21 = 336$ square yards
$27 \times 15 = 405 \text{ m}^2$ $14 \times 9 = 126$ square yards
$19 \times 8 = 152 \text{ m}^2$ $31 \times 22 = 682$ square yards
$62 \times 56 = 3472$ square feet $11 \times 17 = 187 \text{ m}^2$

Explore

If p = 20 cm, l + b = 10 cm.
Possibilities are rectangles: 1 cm × 9 cm, 2 cm × 8 cm, 3 cm × 7 cm,
4 cm × 6 cm, 5 cm × 5 cm (5 rectangles).
If p = 40 cm, l + b = 20 cm.
Possibilities are rectangles: 1 cm × 19 cm, 2 cm × 18 cm, 3 cm × 17 cm,
4 cm × 16 cm, 5 cm × 15 cm, 6 cm × 14 cm, 7 cm × 13 cm, 8 cm × 12 cm,
9 cm × 11 cm, 10 cm × 10 cm (10 rectangles).
If p = 80 cm, there will be $\frac{1}{4}$ x 80 different rectangles i.e. 20 altogether:
1 cm × 39 cm, 2 cm × 38 cm, 3 cm × 37 cm, … 19 cm × 21 cm, 20 cm × 20 cm.

---

page 19
Perimeter of irregular shapes

1. $60 + 60 + 60 + 80 + 120 + 140 = 520$ cm
2. $50 + 60 + 60 + 40 + 110 + 100 = 420$ cm
3. $88 + 75 + 23 + 15 + 42 + 15 + 23 + 75 = 356$ cm
4. $94 + 35 + 68 + 23 + 26 + 58 = 304$ cm
5. $24 + 8 + 9 + 3 + 9 + 12 + 24 + 23 = 112$ cm
6. $48 + 21 + 17 + 19 + 17 + 21 + 48 + 61 = 252$ cm
7. $12 + 8 + 23 + 18 + 35 + 26 = 122$ cm
8. $49 + 58 + 11 + 27 + 27 + 27 + 11 + 58 = 268$ cm
9. $35 + 22 + 25 + 38 + 25 + 30 + 35 + 90 = 300$ cm

e
1. 13 200 cm²   **2.** 7400 cm²   **3.** 5970 cm²
4. 3888 cm²   **5.** 525 cm²   **6.** 2605 cm²
7. 726 cm²   **8.** 2113 cm²   **9.** 4100 cm²

Explore
Answers will vary.

page 20
Perimeter of irregular shapes

1. page: $50 + 30 + 38 + 16 + 12 + 14 = 160$ cm

Shape, Data and Measures

missing piece: $(12 + 16) \times 2 = 56$ cm

2. page: $60 + 40 + 21 + 18 + 15 + 18 + 24 + 40 = 236$ cm
   missing piece: $(15 + 18) \times 2 = 66$ cm
3. page: $17 + 31 + 18 + 24 + 35 + 55 = 180$ cm
   missing piece: $(31 + 18) \times 2 = 98$ cm
4. page: $(56 + 34) \times 2 = 180$ cm
   missing piece: $(23 + 18) \times 2 = 82$ cm
5. page: $(48 + 32) \times 2 = 160$ cm
   missing piece: $(17 + 18) \times 2 = 70$ cm
6. page: $66 + 42 + 15 + 9 + 33 + 9 + 18 + 42 = 234$ cm
   missing piece: $(9 + 33) \times 2 = 84$ cm

1. 1308 cm²   2. 2130 cm²   3. 1367 cm²   4. 1490 cm²
5. 1230 cm²   6. 2475 cm²

Problems

7.

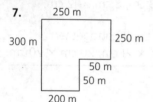

new perimeter = $300 + 250 + 250 + 50 + 50 + 200$
= 1100 m
original area = 300 m $\times$ 250 m = $75\,000$ m²
new area = $75\,000$ m² $- (50$ m $\times 50$ m$) = 72\,500$ m²

8. 2 possible answers: $12'' \times 8''$ basic rectangle with either a $6'' \times 4''$ or
$4'' \times 6''$ piece removed.

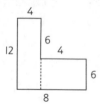

p = $12 + 4 + 6 + 4 + 6 + 8 = 40$ inches
a = $(12 \times 4) + (4 \times 6) = 48 + 24 = 72$ square inches

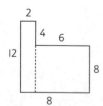

p = $12 + 2 + 4 + 6 + 8 + 8 = 40$ inches
a = $(12 \times 2) + (6 \times 8) = 24 + 48 = 72$ square inches

Shape, Data and Measures

page 21
Mixed problems

1. 0·17 m = 17 cm   The bird is 17 cm tall.
2. 250 g × 7 = 1750 g = 1·75 kg   The dog eats 1·75 kg of food in a week.
3. 15 cm × 7 = 105 cm = 1·05 m   0·86 m + 1·05 m = 1·91 m
   The river is 1·91 m deep.
4. 2 p.m. in Dublin → 8 a.m. in Chicago   Brad is eating breakfast.
   6 p.m. Chicago → midnight Dublin
5. 8 oz margarine ≈ 200 g
   6 oz sugar ≈ 150 g
   12 oz oats ≈ 300 g
   For 3 times as much flapjack:
   24 oz = 1 lb 10 oz ≈ 600 g margarine
   18 oz = 1 lb 4 oz ≈ 450 g sugar
   9 tablespoons syrup
   36 oz = 2 lb 8 oz = $2\frac{1}{2}$ lb ≈ 900 g oats
   3 pinches of salt
6. 44 mm = 0·044 m   0·606 l = 60·6 cl   45 km ≈ 27 miles
   3960 seconds = 1 hour 6 minutes   45 g = 0·045 kg
   0·53 km = 530 m   465 cl = 4650 ml   5475 kg = 5·475 tonnes
7. 8 a.m. London → 1:30 p.m. Delhi
   flight time = $8\frac{1}{2}$ hours $10 - 1\frac{1}{2} = 8\frac{1}{2}$
8. Children will need to draw two graphs.

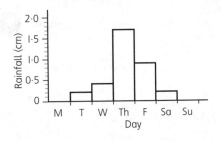

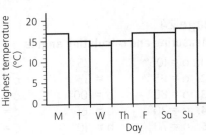

---

page 22

Measuring and drawing angles

1. 81°   2. 112°   3. 124°   4. 42°   5. 143°
6. 54°   7. 138°   8. 99°

Shape, Data and Measures

page 22 cont ...

9. 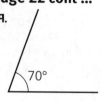 70°

10. 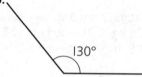 130°

11. 52°

12.  147°

13. 102°

14. 210°

---

page 23

Measuring and calculating angles

1. 125°   2. 110°   3. 100°   4. 120°   5. 105°
6. 130°   7. 125°   8. 130°

9. red 130°   blue 165°   yellow 65°
10. red 120°   blue 120°   yellow 120°
11. red 73°   blue 129°   yellow 158°

---

page 24

Measuring and calculating angles

1. a = 105°   b = 75°   c = 105°
2. a = 115°   b = 65°   c = 115°
3. a = 80°   b = 100°   c = 80°
4. a = 20°   b = 160°   c = 20°
5. a = 70°   b = 110°   c = 70°
6. a = 50°   b = 130°   c = 50°
7. a = 140°   b = 40°   c = 140°
8. a = 125°   b = 55°   c = 125°
9. a = 95°   b = 85°   c = 95°

Explore

Opposite angles are always equal. There are 2 pairs of equal opposite angles.

Shape, Data and Measures

page 25

Measuring and calculating angles

1.	$a = 60°$	$b = 60°$	$c = 60°$	total 180°
2.	$a = 50°$	$b = 50°$	$c = 80°$	total 180°
3.	$a = 35°$	$b = 35°$	$c = 110°$	total 180°
4.	$a = 90°$	$b = 45°$	$c = 45°$	total 180°
5.	$a = 90°$	$b = 45°$	$c = 45°$	total 180°

Explore

The sum of the angles in any triangle is always 180°.

page 26

Measuring and calculating angles

1.	$90° + 30° = 120°$	$180° − 120° = 60°$
2.	$90° + 45° = 135°$	$180° − 135° = 45°$
3.	$90° + 50° = 140°$	$180° − 140° = 40°$
4.	$90° + 35° = 125°$	$180° − 125° = 55°$
5.	$90° + 70° = 160°$	$180° − 160° = 20°$
6.	$90° + 40° = 130°$	$180° − 130° = 50°$
7.	$90° + 60° = 150°$	$180° − 150° = 30°$
8.	$90° + 25° = 115°$	$180° − 115° = 65°$
9.	$90° + 55° = 145°$	$180° − 145° = 35°$
10.	$50° + 80° = 130°$	$180° − 130° = 50°$
11.	$80° + 45° = 125°$	$180° − 125° = 55°$
12.	$95° + 30° = 125°$	$180° − 125° = 55°$
13.	$110° + 30° = 140°$	$180° − 140° = 40°$
14.	$30° + 70° = 100°$	$180° − 100° = 80°$

page 27

Measuring and calculating angles

1.	$a = 65°$	$b = 65°$	2.	$a = 75°$	$b = 75°$
3.	$a = 70°$	$b = 70°$	4.	$a = 35°$	$b = 35°$
5.	$a = 50°$	$b = 50°$	6.	$a = 55°$	$b = 55°$
7.	$a = 90°$	$b = 45°$	8.	$a = 20°$	$b = 80°$
9.	$a = 30°$	$b = 120°$			

Explore

Answers will vary.

Shape, Data and Measures

page 28
Reading and writing coordinates

1. (¯4,¯2)   2. (2,¯3)   3. (¯2,3)   4. (2,3)   5. (¯4,4)
6. (¯5,¯5)   7. (4,1)

8. Pirate Ship   9. Shipwreck Beach   10. Smuggler's Cove
11. Lighthouse   12. Pearl Divers   13. Crashing Cliffs
14. Giant Octopus

✐ Answers will vary.

---

page 29
Reading and writing coordinates

1. Abacus   (-5,5),(¯5,2),(¯2,2),(¯2,5),(¯3,5),(¯3,3), (¯4,3), (¯4,5)
2. Trapezium   (1,3),(2,5),(4,5),(5,3)
3. Pyramid   (¯4,¯1),(¯3,¯3),(¯4,¯4),(¯6,¯4)
4. Kite   (5,¯3),(3,¯2),(2,0),(3,1),(4,0)
5. Flag   (4,¯4),(2,¯5),(4,¯6),(¯1,¯6),(¯1,¯4)

6. square   7. triangle   8. quadrilateral
9. kite   10. trapezium   11. triangle

---

page 30
Coordinates of reflected shapes

1. red (¯2,2)(¯4,1)   blue (4,1)(2,2)   2. red (¯3,1)(¯4,3)   blue (3,1)(2,3)
      (¯4,5)(¯2,4)   (4,5)(2,4)   (¯3,5)(¯2,3)   (3,5)(4,3)

   yellow (¯2,¯2)(¯4,¯1) pink (4,¯1)(2,¯2)   yellow (¯3,1)(¯2,¯3) pink (3,¯1)(2,¯3)
        (¯2,¯4)(¯4,¯5)   (4,¯5)(2,¯4)   (¯3,5)(¯4,¯3)   (3,¯5)(4,¯3)

3. red (¯2,1)(¯2,5)   blue (2,1)(2,5)   4. red (¯2,2)(¯4,1)   blue (2,2)(4,1)
      (¯4,3)   (4,3)   (¯2,5)(¯4,4)   (2,5)(4,4)

   yellow (¯2,¯1)(¯2,¯5) pink (2,¯1)(2,¯5)   yellow (¯4,¯1)(¯2,¯2) pink (4,¯1)(2,¯2)
        (¯4,¯3)   (4,¯3)   (¯4,¯4)(¯2,¯5)   (4,¯4)(2,¯5)

5. red (¯2,1)(¯4,1)   blue (2,1)(4,1)   6. red (¯1,4)(¯3,1)   blue (3,1)(1,4)
      (¯3,5)   (3,5)   (¯5,4)(¯3,5)   (3,5)(5,4)

   yellow (¯3,¯1)(¯2,¯5) pink (3,¯1)(2,¯5)   yellow (¯3,¯1)(¯1,¯4) pink (3,¯1)(1,¯4)
        (¯4,¯5)   (4,¯5)   (¯3,¯5)(¯5,¯4)   (3,¯5)(5,¯4)

Shape, Data and Measures

page 30 cont ...

Explore

All points with x-coordinate greater than y-coordinate lie to the right of the
line y = x.
All points with x-coordinate smaller than y-coordinate lie to the left of the
line y = x.

---

page 31

Reflecting shapes

I.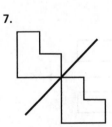

2.

3.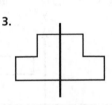

4.

5.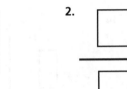

6.

7.

8.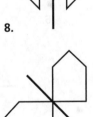

q.

10.

II.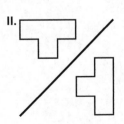

12.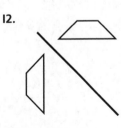

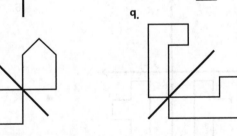

Shape, Data and Measures

page 32

Reflecting coordinates

I. D → (1,4)   **2.** F → (⁻2,⁻4)   **3.** J → (⁻4,5)   **4.** H → (⁻5,0)
5. B → (⁻4,⁻1)   **6.** K → (2,2)   **7.** A → (⁻2,3)   **8.** G → (2,⁻1)
9. C → (1,⁻3)   **10.** L → (0,⁻4)   **II.** E → (⁻2,0)   **12.** I → (0,3)

@

I. D → (⁻1,⁻4)   **2.** F → (2,4)   **3.** J → (4,⁻5)   **4.** H → (5,0)
5. B → (4,1)   **6.** K → (⁻2,⁻2)   **7.** A → (2,⁻3)   **8.** G → (⁻2,1)
9. C → (⁻1,3)   **10.** L → (0,⁻4)   **II.** E → (2,0)   **12.** I → (0,3)

13.

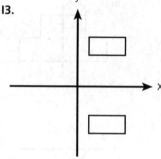

14.

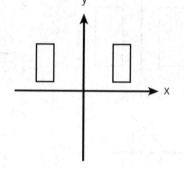

15.

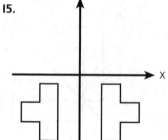

16.

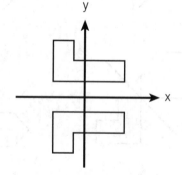

Shape, Data and Measures

Reflections in two mirror lines

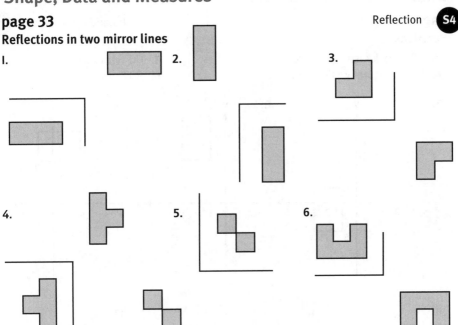

Explore

Answers will vary.

The reflection in two mirrors is the same as a 180° rotation about the meeting point of the mirrors.

Translations

1. A (4,0)   **2.** C (2,⁻1)   **3.** D (⁻3,4)   **4.** B (9,⁻1)   **5.** A (0,7)
6. B (2,4)   **7.** B (8,⁻1)   **8.** C (5,7)

9. 1 unit left, 5 units down   **10.** 6 units right, 4 units down
11. 3 units left, 3 units down   **12.** 4 units left, 4 units down
13. 2 units right, 2 units down   **14.** 5 units left, 1 unit down

@

9. (⁻1,⁻1)(2,⁻1)(2,0)(⁻1,0)   **10.** (⁻4,⁻3)(⁻4,⁻1)(⁻6,⁻3)(⁻6,⁻1)
11. (⁻1,⁻3)(1,⁻3)(⁻1,0)
12. (⁻2,0)(⁻1,0)(⁻1,⁻1)(0,⁻1)(0,⁻2)(⁻1,⁻2)(⁻1,⁻3)(⁻2,⁻3)(⁻2,⁻2)(⁻3,⁻2)(⁻3,⁻1)(⁻2,⁻1)
13. (⁻2,⁻4)(⁻4,⁻4)(⁻2,⁻2)   **14.** (0,⁻3)(1,⁻3)(0,⁻6)(1,⁻6)

Shape, Data and Measures

Rotations

1. 90° clockwise
2. 180°
3. 90° clockwise
4. 90° anticlockwise
5. 180°
6. 90° clockwise

7.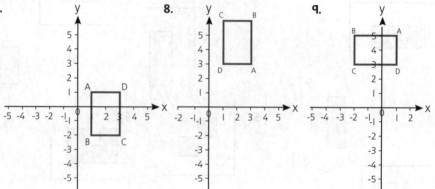

8.

9.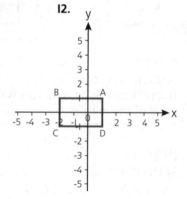

10.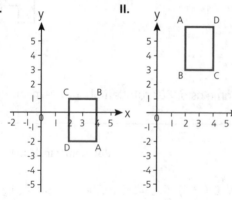

11.

12.

13.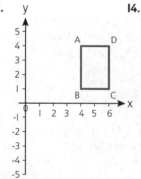

14.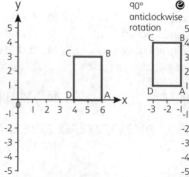

90° anticlockwise rotation

90° clockwise rotation

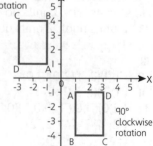

Shape, Data and Measures

page 36
Translations, reflections, rotations

I. (3,⁻3)   **2.** (⁻1,0)   **3.** (3,2)   **4.** (⁻4,2)   **5.** (5,8)
6. (1,0)   **7.** (3,⁻3)   **8.** (⁻1,0)   **q.** (5,4)   **10.** (5,0)

☺
I. (3,1)   **2.** (⁻1,4)   **3.** (7,2)   **4.** (⁻4,6)   **5.** (5,4)
6. (1,⁻4)   **7.** (3,1)   **8.** (⁻1,⁻4)   **q.** (1,4)   **10.** (5,⁻4)

Explore
Other ways include:
Red → Yellow
- a reflection in the y-axis, then a reflection in the x-axis
- a translation of 3 units down and 4 units right

Red → Blue
- a rotation of 90° clockwise about the origin, then a translation of 1 unit right
- a rotation of 90° anticlockwise about the origin, then a translation of 5 units right and 3 units up

Blue → Yellow
- a rotation of 90° clockwise about the origin, then a translation of 1 unit right and 2 units up
- a rotation of 90° anticlockwise about the origin, then a translation of 3 units right and 5 units down

---

page 37
Naming 3-d shapes

A cuboid   B pyramid   C cylinder   D cone   E prism
F pyramid   G cube   H pyramid   I prism   J prism

I. 5   **2.** 8   **3.** 4   **4.** 8   **5.** 6
6. I   **7.** B   **8.** I   **q.** E   **10.** H
II. F   **12.** J   **13.** J

☺ B triangular-based pyramid/tetrahedron   H square-based pyramid
  E hexagonal prism   I triangular prism
  F hexagonal-based pyramid   J pentagonal-based pyramid

Shape, Data and Measures

page 38

Nets of 3-d shapes

1. cube   3 pairs of parallel square faces
2. square-based pyramid   no parallel faces
3. cuboid   2 pairs of parallel rectangular faces, I pair of parallel square faces
4. triangular prism   I pair of parallel triangular faces
5. cuboid   3 pairs of parallel rectangular faces (all different sizes)
6. hexagonal prism   I pair of parallel hexagonal faces
                      3 pairs of parallel rectangular faces

Explore

There are II different nets of cubes. Faces with the same shading will be parallel.

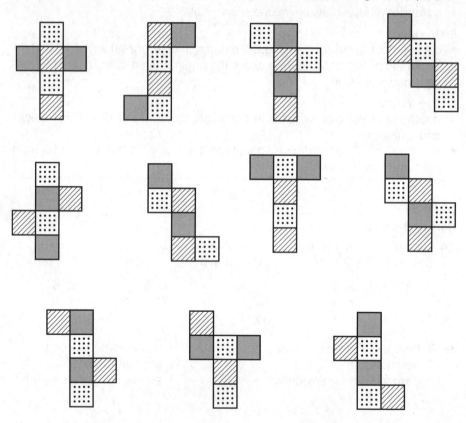

Shape, Data and Measures

page 39

Polyhedra

1. hexahedron (cube)
2. tetrahedron
3. octahedron
4. hexahedron (cuboid)
5. octahedron
6. dodecahedron (12 faces)
7. pentahedron

- 1., 2., 3. and 6. are regular polyhedra.

Explore

Answers will vary.

---

page 40

Parallelograms, rhombuses, trapezia

1. 2 pairs
2. 2 pairs
3. 2 pairs
4. 2 pairs
5. 1 pair
6. 3 pairs
7. 2 pairs
8. 1 pair
9. 2 pairs
10. 2 pairs
11. 2 pairs
12. 2 pairs
13. 4 pairs

a. parallelograms: 1, 3, 7, 10, 12 (2, 4, 9, 11 are squares and rectangles which are also parallelograms)

b rhombuses: 4, 9

Explore

The two triangles will always create a parallelogram.

---

page 41

Parallelograms, rhombuses, trapezia

1. no
2. yes
3. no
4. no
5. yes
6. yes
7. no
8. yes
9. no
10. yes
11. no
12. no
13. no

1a. rectangle
3a. parallelogram
4a. square
7a. square
9a. rectangle
11a. pentagon
12a. parallelogram
13a. pentagon

Explore

Possibilities include: rectangle, parallelogram, trapezium, kite.

Shape, Data and Measures

page 42
Parallelograms, rhombuses, trapezia

1. parallelogram
2. pentagon
3. trapezium
4. parallelogram
5. parallelogram
6. rectangle
7. parallelogram
8. parallelogram
9. trapezium
10. trapezium
11. parallelogram
12. trapezium
13. trapezium

Explore

Answers will vary.

---

page 43
Kites

1. yes
2. no
3. yes
4. no
5. yes
6. no
7. no
8. no
9. yes
10. yes

2a. parallelogram
4a. square
6a. parallelogram
7a. parallelogram
8a. trapezium

Explore

The diagonals of a kite meet at right angles, and they bisect each other.

---

page 44
Quadrilaterals

1. rectangle
2. square
3. trapezium
4. kite
5. parallelogram
6. square
7. trapezium
8. kite
9. rectangle
10. parallelogram
11. kite
12. trapezium
13. trapezium

Explore

Ignoring rotations or reflections as these are the same shape, the 16 possible quadrilaterals are:

Shape, Data and Measures

---

page 45   2-d shape **S8**
Quadrilaterals

quadrilateral	0 parallel sides	1 pair parallel sides	2 pairs parallel sides
square			✓
rectangle			✓
parallelogram			✓
rhombus			✓
trapezium		✓	
kite	✓		

Shape, Data and Measures

quadrilateral	0 equal angles	I pair equal angles	2 pairs equal angles	4 equal angles
square				✓
rectangle				✓
parallelogram			✓	
rhombus			✓	
trapezium	✓	✓ (trapezium with two right-angles)	✓ (isosceles trapezium)	
kite		✓		

quadrilateral	0 equal sides	I pair equal sides	2 pairs equal sides	4 equal sides
square				✓
rectangle			✓	
parallelogram			✓	
rhombus				✓
trapezium	✓	✓ (isosceles trapezium)		
kite			✓	

● square: quadrilateral with all sides and angles equal. All angles 90°.
rectangle: quadrilateral with opposite sides equal and parallel. All angles 90°.
parallelogram: quadrilateral with opposite sides equal and parallel. Opposite angles equal.
rhombus: quadrilateral with all sides equal and opposite sides parallel. Opposite angles equal.
trapezium: quadrilateral with one pair of parallel sides, one longer than the other.
kite: quadrilateral with two pairs of adjacent sides of equal length.

---

page 46
Polygons

I. quadrilateral   2. triangle   3. hexagon   4. hexagon
5. octagon   6. pentagon   7. octagon   8. decagon
9. heptagon   10. heptagon   II. quadrilateral   12. pentagon
13. nonagon

Shape, Data and Measures

page 46 cont ...

@ Shapes 2, 3, 5, 8, 10, 12, 13 are regular.

Answers will vary. Possibilities include:

14.

15.

16.

17.

18.

19.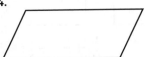

20.

---

page 47
Polygons

1. square inside regular hexagon
2. pentagon inside parallelogram
3. octagon inside trapezium
4. parallelogram inside octagon
5. pentagon inside hexagon
6. nonagon inside rectangle
7. parallelogram inside heptagon
8. square inside square
9. quadrilateral inside triangle
10. triangle inside decagon

Explore

The totals of the angles in different polygons are:

number of sides	angle total
3	2 right angles (180°)
4	4 right angles (360°)
5	6 right angles (540°)
6	8 right angles (720°)
n	2 (n−2) right angles (90n°)

Shape, Data and Measures

page 48
Dissections

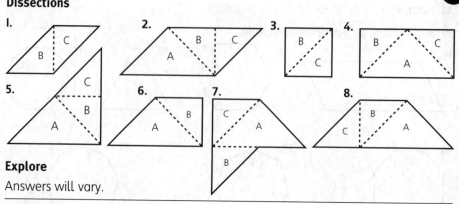

Explore

Answers will vary.

---

page 49
Grouped data

Word length	Frequency
1–3	45
4–6	31
7–9	8
10+	2

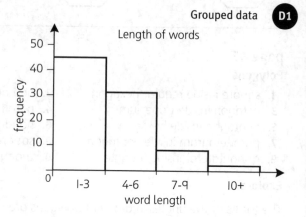

1. 45　　　**2.** 8　　　**3.** 31　　　**4.** 10　　　**5.** 76

Shape, Data and Measures

Grouped data

Score	Frequency
1–5	2
6–10	6
11–15	7
16–20	5
21–25	1
26–30	6

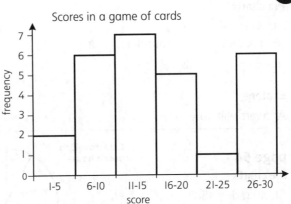

Scores in a game of cards

Explore
Answers will vary.

Grouped data

Score	Frequency
10–12	8
13–15	5
16–18	5
19–21	3
22–24	3

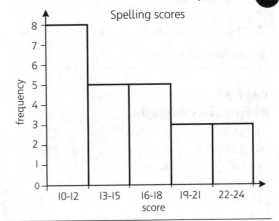

Spelling scores

Explore
Answers will vary.

Pie charts

1. 1
2. 1
3. 2
4. 2
5. 2
6. 3
7. 4
8. Sci-fi
9. Soaps
10. Horror
11. Sports and Adventure
12. $\frac{4}{8} = \frac{1}{2}$
13. $\frac{1}{8}$
14. $\frac{2}{8} = \frac{1}{4}$
15. $\frac{1}{8}$
16. $\frac{2}{8} = \frac{1}{4}$
17. $\frac{3}{8}$
18. $\frac{2}{8} = \frac{1}{4}$

Explore
Answers will vary.

Shape, Data and Measures

page 53
Pie charts

Pie charts **D2**

1. 4
2. 2
3. 1
4. 6
5. 3
6. football
7. rounders
8. $\frac{1}{4}$
9. $\frac{3}{16}$
10. $\frac{3}{8}$
11. $\frac{1}{8}$
12. $\frac{1}{16}$

Explore
Answers will vary.

---

page 54
Pie charts

Pie charts **D2**

Cars travelling past a house

1. 10 red → 150°
2. 7 black → 105°
3. 5 yellow → 75°
4. 2 blue → 30°

5. red
6. blue
7. $\frac{5}{12}$
8. $\frac{5}{24}$
9. $\frac{1}{12}$
10. $\frac{7}{24}$

℮ Answers will vary.

---

page 55
Using conversion graphs

Conversion graphs **D3**

1. $45
2. $60
3. $22·50
4. $52·50
5. $15
6. $37·50
7. £20
8. £10
9. £7
10. £30
11. £23
12. £43

Conversion graph: pounds and rand

13. £2
14. £5
15. £8
16. £17·50
17. £11·50
18. £16·50

---

page 56
Using conversion graphs

Conversion graphs **D3**

1. 86 °F
2. 68 °F
3. 104 °F
4. 58 °F
5. 95 °F
6. 77 °F
7. 27 °C
8. 10 °C
9. 22 °C
10. 35 °C
11. 18 °C
12. 43 °C

Shape, Data and Measures

Month	Jan	Feb	Mar	Apr	May	Jun	Jul	Aug	Sep	Oct	Nov	Dec
Temperature (°C)	2	5	10	16	20	21	25	28	26	18	9	6
Temperature (°F)	35	40	50	60	68	69	77	83	78	65	48	42

page 57   Conversion graphs   **D3**
Using conversion graphs

1. 32 km   **2.** 48 km   **3.** 80 km   **4.** 24 km   **5.** 40 km
6. 72 km   **7.** 25 miles   **8.** 38 miles   **9.** 13 miles   **10.** 9 miles
11. 34 miles   **12.** 47 miles

From Longbridge	To Backton	To Farley	To Weybridge	To Johnston	To Midwich	To Hayes
km	47	32	28	53	76	59
miles	29	20	18	33	48	37

page 58   Averages   **D4**
The mean

1. Blue: $25 \div 5 = 5$ **2.** White: $20 \div 5 = 4$ **3.** Red: $35 \div 5 = 7$
4. Green: $30 \div 5 = 6$ **5.** Yellow: $25 \div 5 = 5$ **6.** Orange: $25 \div 5 = 5$

7. $15 \div 3 = 5$ **8.** $15 \div 3 = 5$ **9.** $18 \div 3 = 6$ **10.** $18 \div 3 = 6$
11. $18 \div 3 = 6$ **12.** $12 \div 3 = 4$ **13.** $40p \div 4 = 10p$ **14.** $30p \div 6 = 5p$
15. $60p \div 3 = 20p$ **16.** $115p \div 5 = 23p$

Shape, Data and Measures

page 59
The mode

1.

shoe size	frequency class 6A
$1\frac{1}{2}$	2
2	5
$2\frac{1}{2}$	7
3	9
$3\frac{1}{2}$	4
4	2
$4\frac{1}{2}$	1
5	0

shoe size	frequency class 6B
$1\frac{1}{2}$	1
2	2
$2\frac{1}{2}$	3
3	6
$3\frac{1}{2}$	8
4	5
$4\frac{1}{2}$	3
5	2

The mode for class 6A is 3, the mode for class 6B is $3\frac{1}{2}$. Class 6B have more people with bigger feet than class 6A.

Explore
Answers will vary.

---

page 60
The median

1. United — 0, 0, 1, 1, 2, 2, 3, 3, 4, 4, 5 — median 2 goals
2. City — 0, 1, 1, 1, 2, 2, 2, 2, 3 — median 2 goals
3. Rangers — 0, 1, 1, 2, 2, 2, 3, 3, 4, 5, 6 — median 2 goals
4. Rovers — 1, 2, 3, 3, 3, 4, 5 — median 3 goals
5. Town — 0, 1, 1, 1, 2, 2, 2, 2, 3, 3, 7 — median 2 goals
6. Wanderers — 1, 1, 2, 2, 2, 3, 3 — median 2 goals
7. Albion — 0, 0, 1, 1, 1, 2, 2, 2, 3, 4 — median 1·5 goals
8. Kickers — 1, 2, 2, 2, 2, 2, 3, 3, 5, 6 — median 2 goals

Explore
Answers will vary.

---

page 61
Mean, median, mode

1. mean $67 \div 20 = 3·35$
2. median 3·5
3. mode 4
4. mean $72 \div 21 = 3·43$
5. median 4
6. mode 5
7. mean $56 \div 15 = 3·73$
8. median 4
9. mode 3

Ⓔ Answers will vary.

Shape, Data and Measures

page 62
Throwing dice

1. $\frac{1}{6}$ of 24 = 4   2. $\frac{1}{6}$ of 24 = 4   3. $\frac{1}{6}$ of 24 = 4   4. $\frac{1}{6}$ of 24 = 4

5. $\frac{1}{6}$ of 24 = 4   6. $\frac{1}{6}$ of 30 = 5   7. $\frac{1}{6}$ of 60 = 10   8. $\frac{1}{6}$ of 18 = 3

9. $\frac{1}{6}$ of 36 = 6   10. $\frac{1}{6}$ of 120 = 20   11. $\frac{1}{2}$ of 18 = 9   12. $\frac{1}{2}$ of 18 = 9

13. $\frac{1}{2}$ of 12 = 6   14. $\frac{1}{2}$ of 24 = 12   15. $\frac{1}{2}$ of 50 = 25   16. $\frac{1}{2}$ of 44 = 22

17. $\frac{1}{2}$ of 110 = 55

page 63
Probability

Event	Chance	Probability
1. a 2	1 in 6	$\frac{1}{6}$
2. a 5	1 in 6	$\frac{1}{6}$
3. an odd	3 in 6	$\frac{3}{6} = \frac{1}{2}$
4. more than 3	3 in 6	$\frac{3}{6} = \frac{1}{2}$
5. less than 5	4 in 6	$\frac{4}{6} = \frac{2}{3}$
6. 2 or more	5 in 6	$\frac{5}{6}$
7. a 7	0 in 6	0
8. an even	3 in 6	$\frac{3}{6} = \frac{1}{2}$
9. less than 7	6 in 6	1

Answers will vary.

Shape, Data and Measures

Probability

Event	Chance	Probability	Letter on probability scale	Prediction for 40 goes
1. yellow	4 in 10	$\frac{4}{10} = \frac{2}{5}$	e	1a. 16
2. red	1 in 10	$\frac{1}{10}$	b	2a. 4
3. pink	3 in 10	$\frac{3}{10}$	d	3a. 12
4. blue	2 in 10	$\frac{2}{10} = \frac{1}{5}$	c	4a. 8
5. red or yellow	5 in 10	$\frac{5}{10} = \frac{1}{2}$	f	5a. 20
6. pink or blue	5 in 10	$\frac{5}{10} = \frac{1}{2}$	f	6a. 20
7. blue or red	3 in 10	$\frac{3}{10}$	d	7a. 12
8. not red	9 in 10	$\frac{9}{10}$	j	8a. 36
9. green	0 in 10	0	a	9a. 0
10. not blue	8 in 10	$\frac{8}{10} = \frac{4}{5}$	i	10a. 32
11. not pink	7 in 10	$\frac{7}{10}$	h	11a. 28
12. not yellow	6 in 10	$\frac{6}{10} = \frac{3}{5}$	g	12a. 24

Answers will vary.

Photocopy Masters

page 1

Rounding decimals

Movements (roundings) as follows:

3·3 → 3 (start)	3·6 → 4	3·9 → 4
4·2 → 4	4·6 → 5	4·9 → 5
5·3 → 5	5·6 → 6	5·9 → 6
6·5 → 7	6·6 → 7	6·7 → 7
7·2 → 7	7·5 → 8	7·9 → 8
8·3 → 8	8·6 → 9 (finish)	

page 3
Place-value **N1**

Nearest whole number

nearest whole number	3,5,2,8	4,6,1,7	2,9,0,4	3,4,6,7
1	2·35	1·46	0·94	3·46
2	2·35	1·76	2·04	3·46
3	2·85	4·17	2·94	3·46
4	3·85	4·17	4·02	3·76
5	5·23	4·76	4·92	4·76
6	5·83	6·14	4·92	6·34
7	5·83	7·14	9·02	6·74
8	8·23	7·64	9·02	7·64
9	8·53	7·64	9·02	7·64
10	8·53	7·64	9·42	7·64

page 4
Place-value **N2**

Dividing by 10 and 100

1. £38 ÷ 10 = £3·80
2. £72 ÷ 10 = £7·20
3. £60 ÷ 10 = £6·00
4. £95 ÷ 10 = £9·50
5. £4 ÷ 10 = £0·40 = 40p
6. £53 ÷ 10 = £5·30
7. £421 ÷ 100 = £4·21
8. £360 ÷ 100 = £3·60
9. £725 ÷ 100 = £7·25
10. £582 ÷ 100 = £5·82
11. £109 ÷ 100 = £1·09
12. £470 ÷ 100 = £4·70

Photocopy Masters

page 5

Dividing by 10 and 100

1. $46 \div 10 = 4 \cdot 6$
2. $28 \div 10 = 2 \cdot 8$
3. $73 \div 10 = 7 \cdot 3$
4. $6 \div 10 = 0 \cdot 6$
5. $15 \div 10 = 1 \cdot 5$
6. $55 \div 10 = 5 \cdot 5$
7. $236 \div 100 = 2 \cdot 36$
8. $478 \div 100 = 4 \cdot 78$
9. $504 \div 100 = 5 \cdot 04$
10. $732 \div 100 = 7 \cdot 32$
11. $62 \div 100 = 0 \cdot 62$
12. $58 \div 100 = 0 \cdot 58$
13. $7 \div 100 = 0 \cdot 07$
14. $11 \div 100 = 0 \cdot 11$
15. $1 \cdot 4 \div 10 = 0 \cdot 14$
16. $2 \div 100 = 0 \cdot 02$
17. $37 \div 10 = 3 \cdot 7$
18. $158 \div 100 = 1 \cdot 58$
19. $42 \div 100 = 0 \cdot 42$
20. $63 \cdot 1 \div 10 = 6 \cdot 31$

page 6

Division facts

1. $30 \div 6 = 5$
2. $32 \div 4 = 8$
3. $48 \div 6 = 8$
4. $54 \div 6 = 9$
5. $45 \div 5 = 9$
6. $56 \div 8 = 7$
7. $21 \div 7 = 3$
8. $27 \div 9 = 3$
9. $24 \div 3 = 8$
10. $35 \div 5 = 7$
11. $49 \div 7 = 7$
12. $40 \div 8 = 5$
13. $72 \div 9 = 8$
14. $16 \div 4 = 4$
15. $63 \div 7 = 9$
16. $64 \div 8 = 8$
17. $36 \div 4 = 9$
18. $81 \div 9 = 9$
19. $42 \div 7 = 6$
20. $63 \div 9 = 7$

page 8

Multiplication facts

1.

×	2	3	4	5
2	4	6	8	10
3	6	9	12	15
4	8	12	16	20
5	10	15	20	25

2.

×	4	5	6	7
4	16	20	24	28
5	20	25	30	35
6	24	30	36	42
7	28	35	42	49

3.

×	7	8	9	2
3	21	24	27	6
4	28	32	36	8
5	35	40	45	10
6	42	48	54	12

4.

×	2	3	4	5
6	12	18	24	30
7	14	21	28	35
8	16	24	32	40
9	18	27	36	45

Photocopy Masters

5.

×	5	3	6	4
7	35	21	42	28
2	10	6	12	8
8	40	24	48	32
9	45	27	54	36

6.

×	3	1	4	7
6	18	6	24	42
0	0	0	0	0
8	24	8	32	56
5	15	5	20	35

7.

×	3	4	6	5
2	6	8	12	10
8	24	32	48	40
6	18	24	36	30
9	27	36	54	45

8.

×	2	4	8	7
5	10	20	40	35
7	14	28	56	49
9	18	36	72	63
3	6	12	24	21

9.

×	6	2	7	9
8	48	16	56	72
3	18	6	21	27
5	30	10	35	45
4	24	8	28	36

---

page 9   Multiplication/division N3
Card multiplications

There are many possible answers.
For example:

$2 \times 3 = 6$	$2 \times 4 = 8$	$2 \times 5 = 10$	$2 \times 7 = 14$	$2 \times 8 = 16$	$2 \times 9 = 18$
$3 \times 4 = 12$	$3 \times 6 = 18$	$3 \times 7 = 21$	$3 \times 8 = 24$	$3 \times 9 = 27$	
$4 \times 5 = 20$	$4 \times 7 = 28$	$4 \times 8 = 32$	$4 \times 9 = 36$		
$5 \times 6 = 30$	$5 \times 8 = 40$				
$6 \times 7 = 42$	$6 \times 9 = 54$				
$7 \times 8 = 56$	$7 \times 9 = 63$				
$8 \times 9 = 72$	etc.				

Photocopy Masters

Halving and doubling

2·6	7·6	5·9
6·4	3·4	4·7
8·3	1·9	7·2

→

5·2	15·2	11·8
12·8	6·8	9·4
16·6	3·8	14·4

3400	290	7600
470	4600	630
3800	390	8200

→

1700	145	3800
235	2300	315
1900	195	4100

9·6	13·4	13·4
7·8	12·5	15·7
3·9	4·6	7·8

→

19·2	26·8	26·8
15·6	25·0	31·4
7·8	9·2	15·6

Multiplication tables

1.

×	4	6	5	7	3
10	40	60	50	70	30
30	120	180	150	210	90
50	200	300	250	350	150
40	160	240	200	280	120
20	80	120	100	140	60

2.

×	50	90	60	80	70
2	100	180	120	160	140
5	250	450	300	400	350
4	200	360	240	320	280
6	300	540	360	480	420
3	150	270	180	240	210

Photocopy Masters

3.

×	3	5	7	4	6
200	600	1000	1400	800	1200
500	1500	2500	3500	2000	3000
300	900	1500	2100	1200	1800
100	300	500	700	400	600
400	1200	2000	2800	1600	2400

4.

×	600	800	500	700	900
2	1200	1600	1000	1400	1800
5	3000	4000	2500	3500	4500
3	1800	2400	1500	2100	2700
6	3600	4800	3000	4200	5400
4	2400	3200	2000	2800	3600

---

page 12
Multiplication/division **N5**
Multiplying

1. $100 \times 71 = 7100$ $99 \times 71 = 7029$
2. $100 \times 36 = 3600$ $103 \times 36 = 3708$
3. $100 \times 46 = 4600$ $98 \times 46 = 4508$
4. $100 \times 27 = 2700$ $102 \times 27 = 2754$
5. $100 \times 78 = 7800$ $98 \times 78 = 7644$
6. $100 \times 39 = 3900$ $101 \times 39 = 3939$
7. $100 \times 65 = 6500$ $99 \times 65 = 6435$
8. $100 \times 35 = 3500$ $103 \times 35 = 3605$
9. $100 \times 62 = 6200$ $97 \times 62 = 6014$
10. $100 \times 36 = 3600$ $98 \times 36 = 3528$
11. $100 \times 31 = 3100$ $103 \times 31 = 3193$
12. $100 \times 19 = 1900$ $95 \times 19 = 1805$

---

page 13
Multiplication/division **N5**
Dice multiplying

Answers will vary (36 possible combinations of dice for each sum).

Photocopy Masters

page 14
Multiplying by doubling

1. $7 \times 6 = 42 \rightarrow 7 \times 12 = 84$
2. $8 \times 9 = 72 \rightarrow 8 \times 18 = 144$
3. $6 \times 7 = 42 \rightarrow 6 \times 14 = 84$
4. $4 \times 8 = 32 \rightarrow 4 \times 16 = 64$
5. $9 \times 6 = 54 \rightarrow 9 \times 12 = 108$
6. $3 \times 9 = 27 \rightarrow 3 \times 36 = 108$
7. $9 \times 8 = 72 \rightarrow 9 \times 32 = 288$
8. $5 \times 7 = 35 \rightarrow 5 \times 28 = 140$
9. $8 \times 6 = 48 \rightarrow 8 \times 24 = 192$
10. $7 \times 4 = 28 \rightarrow 7 \times 16 = 112$
11. $11 \times 7 = 77 \rightarrow 11 \times 14 = 154$
12. $6 \times 6 = 36 \rightarrow 6 \times 48 = 288$

page 15
Fraction wheels

1. £24, £28, £10, £12, £16, £22
2. £24, £22, £21, £16, £30, £27
3. £15, £32, £30, £25, £22, £28
4. £30, £10, £36, £24, £35, £27
5. £42, £24, £55, £50, £40, £39
6. £48, £54, £60, £63, £32, £42

page 16
Equivalent fractions

1. $\frac{1}{2} = \frac{2}{4} = \frac{3}{6} = \frac{4}{8} = \frac{7}{14}$
2. $\frac{1}{5} = \frac{2}{10} = \frac{3}{15} = \frac{5}{25} = \frac{6}{30}$
3. $\frac{3}{4} = \frac{6}{8} = \frac{9}{12} = \frac{12}{16} = \frac{18}{24}$
4. $\frac{2}{3} = \frac{4}{6} = \frac{6}{9} = \frac{8}{12} = \frac{10}{15}$
5. $\frac{3}{5} = \frac{6}{10} = \frac{9}{15} = \frac{12}{20} = \frac{18}{30}$
6. $\frac{3}{10} = \frac{6}{20} = \frac{9}{30} = \frac{12}{40} = \frac{15}{50}$
7. $\frac{1}{4} = \frac{2}{8} = \frac{4}{16} = \frac{5}{20} = \frac{10}{40}$

page 18
Reducing fractions

1. $\frac{8}{12} = \frac{2}{3}$
2. $\frac{6}{10} = \frac{3}{5}$
3. $\frac{4}{16} = \frac{1}{4}$
4. $\frac{4}{32} = \frac{1}{8}$
5. $\frac{4}{6} = \frac{2}{3}$
6. $\frac{9}{12} = \frac{3}{4}$
7. $\frac{21}{24} = \frac{7}{8}$
8. $\frac{8}{10} = \frac{4}{5}$
9. $\frac{12}{32} = \frac{3}{8}$
10. $\frac{2}{6} = \frac{1}{3}$
11. $\frac{25}{40} = \frac{5}{8}$
12. $\frac{15}{50} = \frac{3}{10}$
13. $\frac{42}{60} = \frac{7}{10}$
14. $\frac{15}{20} = \frac{3}{4}$
15. $\frac{4}{10} = \frac{2}{5}$
16. $\frac{18}{45} = \frac{2}{5}$
17. $\frac{24}{40} = \frac{3}{5}$
18. $\frac{7}{42} = \frac{1}{6}$
19. $\frac{63}{90} = \frac{7}{10}$
20. $\frac{20}{24} = \frac{5}{6}$
21. $\frac{14}{24} = \frac{7}{12}$
22. $\frac{75}{100} = \frac{3}{4}$
23. $\frac{33}{36} = \frac{11}{12}$
24. $\frac{22}{50} = \frac{11}{25}$

Photocopy Masters

Ordering fractions

A $\frac{2}{3} = \frac{16}{24}$; B $\frac{3}{4} = \frac{18}{24}$; C $\frac{1}{2} = \frac{12}{24}$; D $\frac{5}{6} = \frac{20}{24}$; E $\frac{3}{8} = \frac{9}{24}$
correct order E, C, A, B, D

A $\frac{3}{4} = \frac{15}{20}$; B $\frac{1}{2} = \frac{10}{20}$; C $\frac{1}{4} = \frac{5}{20}$; D $\frac{4}{5} = \frac{16}{20}$; E $\frac{7}{10} = \frac{14}{20}$
correct order C, B, E, A, D

A $\frac{3}{5} = \frac{18}{30}$; B $\frac{5}{6} = \frac{25}{30}$; C $\frac{1}{2} = \frac{15}{30}$; D $\frac{2}{3} = \frac{20}{30}$; E $\frac{11}{15} = \frac{22}{30}$
correct order C, A, D, E, B

A $\frac{2}{5} = \frac{40}{100}$; B $\frac{7}{20} = \frac{35}{100}$; C $\frac{3}{10} = \frac{30}{100}$; D $\frac{1}{4} = \frac{25}{100}$; E $\frac{8}{25} = \frac{32}{100}$
correct order D, C, E, B, A

Comparing fractions

Many possible equivalents.

1. $\frac{2}{3} > \frac{1}{2}$ 2. $\frac{1}{4} < \frac{1}{3}$ 3. $\frac{3}{5} > \frac{1}{2}$ 4. $\frac{3}{5} < \frac{7}{10}$

5. $\frac{2}{3} < \frac{4}{5}$ 6. $\frac{1}{2} < \frac{3}{4}$ 7. $\frac{5}{6} > \frac{3}{4}$ 8. $\frac{3}{4} < \frac{4}{5}$

9. $\frac{1}{3} < \frac{5}{6}$ 10. $\frac{5}{6} < \frac{11}{12}$ 11. $\frac{3}{4} > \frac{5}{8}$ 12. $\frac{5}{6} > \frac{4}{9}$

Adding to 1000

600	100	400
300	250	850
750	350	500

makes 1000 →

400	900	600
700	750	150
250	650	500

140	830	370
510	260	690
720	480	910

makes 1000 →

860	170	630
490	740	310
280	520	90

437	907	256
596	475	328
843	666	172

makes 1000 →

563	93	744
404	525	672
157	334	828

Photocopy Masters

page 22

Car mileage

1. $324 \cdot 6 + 5 \cdot 4 = 330 \cdot 0$
2. $108 \cdot 3 + 1 \cdot 7 = 110 \cdot 0$
3. $15 \cdot 4 + 4 \cdot 6 = 20 \cdot 0$
4. $260 \cdot 5 + 9 \cdot 5 = 270 \cdot 0$
5. $371 \cdot 9 + 8 \cdot 1 = 380 \cdot 0$
6. $428 \cdot 7 + 1 \cdot 3 = 430 \cdot 0$
7. $34 \cdot 6 + 5 \cdot 4 = 40 \cdot 0$
8. $117 \cdot 3 + 2 \cdot 7 = 120 \cdot 0$
9. $63 \cdot 6 + 6 \cdot 4 = 70 \cdot 0$
10. $341 \cdot 7 + 8 \cdot 3 = 350 \cdot 0$
11. $892 \cdot 8 + 7 \cdot 2 = 900 \cdot 0$
12. $278 \cdot 5 + 1 \cdot 5 = 280 \cdot 0$

page 24
Adding several numbers

11	29	9	17	66
32	25	19	27	103
34	28	21	52	135
46	26	37	15	124
123	108	86	111	

23	37	9	27	96
8	24	35	25	92
28	21	36	18	103
34	26	19	29	108
93	108	99	99	

15	23	7	21	66
8	24	32	16	80
22	6	19	9	56
17	25	31	23	96
62	78	89	69	

19	33	21	16	89
23	24	18	32	97
15	36	22	41	114
25	17	31	14	87
82	110	92	103	

page 25
Difference tables

d	178	347	465	218
129	49	218	336	89
364	186	17	101	146
289	111	58	176	71
542	364	195	77	324

d	29	179	17	358
453	424	274	436	95
13	16	166	4	345
562	533	383	545	204
26	3	153	9	332

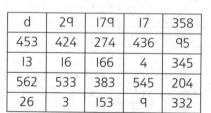

Photocopy Masters

Multiples

1. 3	6	9	12	15	18	21	24
2. 7	14	21	28	35	42	49	56
3. 4	8	12	16	20	24	28	32
4. 9	18	27	36	45	54	63	72
5. 5	10	15	20	25	30	35	40
6. 6	12	18	24	30	36	42	48
7. 8	16	24	32	40	48	56	64
8. 15	30	45	60	75	90	105	120
9. 20	40	60	80	100	120	140	160
10. 12	24	36	48	60	72	84	96

Lowest common multiple

1.

	2	3	5
4	4	12	20
6	6	6	30
7	14	21	35

2.

	2	7	8
5	10	35	40
3	6	21	24
9	18	63	72

3.

	4	5	6
3	12	15	6
7	28	35	42
8	8	40	24

4.

	8	2	7
5	40	10	35
9	72	18	63
6	24	6	42

Dividing by 3

1. 29 ✗	**2.** 35 ✗	**3.** 46 ✗	**4.** 82 ✗	**5.** 91 ✗
6. 135 ✓	**7.** 248 ✗	**8.** 369 ✓	**9.** 172 ✗	**10.** 451 ✗
11. 219 ✓	**12.** 1327 ✗	**13.** 536 ✗	**14.** 248 ✗	**15.** 318 ✓
16. 416 ✗	**17.** 524 ✗	**18.** 369 ✗	**19.** 384 ✓	**20.** 168 ✓
21. 357 ✗	**22.** 408 ✓	**23.** 591 ✗	**24.** 621 ✗	

Photocopy Masters

page 30
Divisibility

Properties of number **N14**

	÷ 2	÷ 3	÷ 4	÷ 5	÷ 6	÷ 8	÷ 9	÷ 10
40	✓		✓	✓		✓		✓
54	✓	✓			✓		✓	
68	✓		✓					
84	✓	✓	✓		✓			
92	✓		✓					
112	✓		✓			✓		
235				✓				
468	✓	✓	✓		✓		✓	

page 31
Multiplying decimals by 10

Place-value **N15**

1. $2.3 \times 10 = 23$
2. $4.5 \times 10 = 45$
3. $0.7 \times 10 = 7$
4. $4.0 \times 10 = 40$
5. $3.7 \times 10 = 37$
6. $17.2 \times 10 = 172$
7. $23.4 \times 10 = 234$
8. $15.6 \times 10 = 156$
9. $7.3 \times 10 = 73$
10. $5.4 \times 10 = 54$
11. $0.6 \times 10 = 6$
12. $3.3 \times 10 = 33$

page 32
Multiplying decimals by 100

Place-value **N15**

1. 2.3 m = 230 cm
2. 1.7 m = 170 cm
3. 6 m = 600 cm
4. 4.8 m = 480 cm
5. 5.32 m = 532 cm
6. 4.06 m = 406 cm
7. 7.00 m = 700 cm
8. $8\frac{1}{2}$ m = 850 cm
9. 1.39 m = 139 cm

page 33
Multiplying decimals by 10 and 100

Place-value **N15**

1. $2.4 \times 10 = 24.0$
2. $3.6 \times 10 = 36.0$
3. $4.7 \times 10 = 47.0$
4. $5.3 \times 10 = 53.0$
5. $0.4 \times 10 = 4.0$
6. $7.0 \times 10 = 70.0$
7. $3.5 \times 100 = 350.0$
8. $1.8 \times 100 = 180.0$
9. $4.72 \times 100 = 472.0$
10. $5.36 \times 100 = 536.0$
11. $7.29 \times 10 = 72.9$
12. $12.7 \times 10 = 127.0$
13. $14.6 \times 10 = 146.0$
14. $3.56 \times 10 = 35.6$
15. $10 \times 3.8 = 38.0$
16. $10 \times 4.9 = 49.0$
17. $100 \times 3.81 = 381.0$
18. $100 \times 0.465 = 46.5$

Photocopy Masters

page 34

Dividing decimals by 10 and 100

1. $123 \div 10 = 12\cdot3$ **2.** $47\cdot6 \div 10 = 4\cdot76$ **3.** $58 \div 100 = 0\cdot58$
4. $9\cdot7 \div 10 = 0\cdot97$ **5.** $19 \div 100 = 0\cdot19$ **6.** $4600 \div 1000 = 4\cdot600$
7. $501 \div 10 = 50\cdot1$ **8.** $0\cdot6 \div 10 = 0\cdot06$ **9.** $11\cdot3 \div 100 = 0\cdot113$
10. $8 \div 10 = 0\cdot8$ **11.** $76\cdot1 \div 10 = 7\cdot61$ **12.** $3 \div 100 = 0\cdot03$
13. $63\cdot5 \div 10 = 6\cdot35$ **14.** $70 \div 100 = 0\cdot7$ **15.** $13\cdot8 \div 10 = 1\cdot38$

---

page 35

Target multiplication

Children's answers will vary.
Closest possible multiplication for each target (using each card only once):

200 $8 \times 25 = 200$ difference 0
160 $5 \times 32 = 160$ difference 0
280 $4 \times 71 = 284$ or $4 \times 69 = 276$ difference 4
95 $5 \times 19 = 95$ difference 0
145 $5 \times 29 = 145$ difference 0
430 $5 \times 86 = 430$ difference 0
350 $6 \times 58 = 348$ difference 2
190 $2 \times 95 = 190$ difference 0
100 $4 \times 25 = 100$ difference 0
495 $6 \times 82 = 492$ or $6 \times 83 = 498$ difference 3

---

page 36

Dice multiplying

Answers will vary. All possible solutions are listed.

1. $2 \times 143 = 286$ $3 \times 143 = 429$ $4 \times 143 = 572$ $5 \times 143 = 715$
$6 \times 143 = 858$

2. $2 \times 265 = 530$ $3 \times 265 = 795$ $4 \times 265 = 1060$ $5 \times 265 = 1325$
$6 \times 265 = 1590$

3. $2 \times 371 = 742$ $3 \times 371 = 1113$ $4 \times 371 = 1484$ $5 \times 371 = 1855$
$6 \times 371 = 2226$

4. $2 \times 536 = 1072$ $3 \times 536 = 1608$ $4 \times 536 = 2144$ $5 \times 536 = 2680$
$6 \times 536 = 3216$

5. $2 \times 219 = 438$ $3 \times 219 = 657$ $4 \times 219 = 876$ $5 \times 219 = 1095$
$6 \times 219 = 1314$

6. $2 \times 391 = 782$ $3 \times 391 = 1173$ $4 \times 391 = 1564$ $5 \times 391 = 1955$
$6 \times 391 = 2346$

Photocopy Masters

page 36 cont ...

7. $2 \times 644 = 1288$ $3 \times 644 = 1932$ $4 \times 644 = 2576$ $5 \times 644 = 3220$
$6 \times 644 = 3864$

8. $2 \times 832 = 1664$ $3 \times 832 = 2496$ $4 \times 832 = 3328$ $5 \times 832 = 4160$
$6 \times 832 = 4992$

9. $2 \times 258 = 516$ $3 \times 258 = 774$ $4 \times 258 = 1032$ $5 \times 258 = 1290$
$6 \times 258 = 1548$

10. $2 \times 444 = 888$ $3 \times 444 = 1332$ $4 \times 444 = 1776$ $5 \times 444 = 2220$
$6 \times 444 = 2664$

page 37
Multiplying by 11

1. $35 \times 11 = 385$ **2.** $23 \times 11 = 253$ **3.** $41 \times 11 = 451$
4. $18 \times 11 = 198$ **5.** $62 \times 11 = 682$ **6.** $54 \times 11 = 594$

page 38
Multiplying

Answers will vary. All possible solutions are listed.

1. $1526 \times 2 = 3052$ $1526 \times 3 = 4578$ $1526 \times 4 = 6104$
$1526 \times 5 = 7630$ $1526 \times 6 = 9156$

2. $2734 \times 2 = 5468$ $2734 \times 3 = 8202$ $2734 \times 4 = 10\,936$
$2734 \times 5 = 13\,670$ $2734 \times 6 = 16\,404$

3. $4163 \times 2 = 8326$ $4163 \times 3 = 12\,489$ $4163 \times 4 = 16\,652$
$4163 \times 5 = 20\,815$ $4163 \times 6 = 24\,978$

4. $5321 \times 2 = 10\,642$ $5321 \times 3 = 15\,963$ $5321 \times 4 = 21\,284$
$5321 \times 5 = 26\,605$ $5321 \times 6 = 31\,926$

5. $2716 \times 2 = 5432$ $2716 \times 3 = 8148$ $2716 \times 4 = 10\,864$
$2716 \times 5 = 13\,580$ $2716 \times 6 = 16\,296$

6. $3847 \times 2 = 7694$ $3847 \times 3 = 11\,541$ $3847 \times 4 = 15\,388$
$3847 \times 5 = 19\,235$ $3847 \times 6 = 23\,082$

page 40
Multiplying

1. $326 \times 42 = 13\,692$ **2.** $326 \times 27 = 8802$ **3.** $496 \times 32 = 15\,872$
4. $271 \times 53 = 14\,363$ **5.** $186 \times 64 = 11\,904$ **6.** $725 \times 19 = 13\,775$

Photocopy Masters

Calculations

1. $13 = 98 \cdot 8 \div 7 \cdot 6$
2. $7 \cdot 6 = 98 \cdot 8 \div 13$
3. $19 = 323 \div 17$
4. $53 \cdot 6 = 6 \cdot 7 \times 8$
5. $26 \cdot 6 = 7 \times 3 \cdot 8$
6. $14 = 1050 \div 75$
7. $4 \cdot 8 = 28 \cdot 8 \div 6$
8. $5 \cdot 4 = 64 \cdot 8 \div 12$
9. $53 \cdot 1 = 5 \cdot 9 \times 9$
10. $75 = 1050 \div 14$
11. $9 = 53 \cdot 1 \div 5 \cdot 9$
12. $7 = 26 \cdot 6 \div 3 \cdot 8$
13. $12 = 64 \cdot 8 \div 5 \cdot 4$
14. $323 = 19 \times 17$
15. $8 = 53 \cdot 6 \div 6 \cdot 7$
16. $6 = 28 \cdot 8 \div 4 \cdot 8$

Remainders

1. $32 \div 3 = 10\frac{2}{3}$
2. $14 \div 5 = 2\frac{4}{5}$
3. $73 \div 2 = 36\frac{1}{2}$
4. $65 \div 4 = 16\frac{1}{4}$
5. $51 \div 6 = 8\frac{1}{2}$
6. $19 \div 3 = 6\frac{1}{3}$
7. $36 \div 5 = 7\frac{1}{5}$
8. $29 \div 4 = 7\frac{1}{4}$
9. $87 \div 8 = 10\frac{7}{8}$
10. $23 \div 9 = 2\frac{5}{9}$
11. $51 \div 2 = 25\frac{1}{2}$
12. $49 \div 5 = 9\frac{4}{5}$
13. $33 \div 6 = 5\frac{1}{2}$
14. $28 \div 3 = 9\frac{1}{3}$
15. $62 \div 5 = 12\frac{2}{5}$
16. $92 \div 8 = 11\frac{1}{2}$
17. $31 \div 4 = 7\frac{3}{4}$
18. $73 \div 7 = 10\frac{3}{7}$
19. $55 \div 8 = 6\frac{7}{8}$
20. $6 \div 9 = \frac{2}{3}$

---

page 44
Multiplication/division N21
Improper fractions

1. $4\frac{3}{4} = \frac{19}{4}$
2. $1\frac{5}{6} = \frac{11}{6}$
3. $2\frac{3}{5} = \frac{13}{5}$
4. $5\frac{1}{2} = \frac{11}{2}$
5. $3\frac{3}{7} = \frac{24}{7}$
6. $7\frac{2}{3} = \frac{23}{3}$
7. $5\frac{5}{8} = \frac{45}{8}$
8. $10\frac{1}{6} = \frac{61}{6}$
9. $2\frac{1}{3} = \frac{7}{3}$
10. $1\frac{4}{9} = \frac{13}{9}$
11. $9\frac{4}{5} = \frac{49}{5}$
12. $13\frac{1}{2} = \frac{27}{2}$
13. $15\frac{7}{9} = \frac{142}{9}$
14. $16\frac{3}{7} = \frac{115}{7}$
15. $7\frac{3}{4} = \frac{31}{4}$
16. $9\frac{7}{8} = \frac{79}{8}$
17. $11\frac{3}{10} = \frac{113}{10}$
18. $4\frac{6}{7} = \frac{34}{7}$

---

page 45
Fractions/decimals N22
Hundredths

| 3·06 | 3·19 | 3·31 | 3·36 | 3·47 | 3·64 | 3·70 | 3·75 | 3·89 | 3·96 |
| 6·11 | 6·18 | 6·27 | 6·42 | 6·50 | 6·54 | 6·62 | 6·70 | 6·82 | 6·87 |

Photocopy Masters

page 46
Hundredths

Any of the following:
0·25   0·28   0·52   0·58   0·82   0·85
Any of the following:
2·03   2·05   2·07
2·30   2·35   2·37
2·50   2·53   2·57
2·70   2·73   2·75

page 47
Ordering hundredths

1. $1·63 > 1·36$ **2.** $4·36 < 4·63$ **3.** $2·35 < 3·25$ **4.** $3\frac{12}{100} < 3·21$

5. $0·5 > \frac{40}{100}$ **6.** $1·3 > 1\frac{27}{100}$ **7.** $4·07 < 4·60$ **8.** $4\frac{11}{100} > 4·1$

9. $5·26 < 5·3$ **10.** $6·4 > 6·39$ **11.** $8\frac{1}{100} < 8·1$ **12.** $7·35 > 5·37$

13. $4·09 < 4·90$ **14.** $6·5 < 6·51$ **15.** $3·89 < 3·9$ **16.** $7·25 < 8$

17. $3·7 < 4·01$ **18.** $5\frac{11}{100} > 5·1$

page 49
Adding 4-digit and 5-digit numbers

1. $3216 + 4532 = 7748$ **2.** $7325 + 1648 = 8973$

3. $2953 + 3748 = 6701$ **4.** $53\,642 + 4719 = 58\,361$

5. $48\,237 + 1958 = 50\,195$ **6.** $17\,326 + 5496 = 22\,822$

7. $4317 + 28\,659 = 32\,976$ **8.** $4549 + 32\,608 = 37\,157$

9. $5907 + 20\,375 = 26\,282$ **10.** $31\,586 + 42\,379 = 73\,965$

11. $58\,219 + 40\,158 = 98\,377$ **12.** $32\,396 + 10\,788 = 43\,184$

page 51
Adding decimal numbers

1. $5·26 + 1·37 = 6·63$ **2.** $4·35 + 2·46 = 6·81$ **3.** $5·39 + 6·48 = 11·87$

4. $7·09 + 5·36 = 12·45$ **5.** $2·87 + 1·94 = 4·81$ **6.** $5·76 + 6·75 = 12·51$

7. $4·52 + 6·73 = 11·25$ **8.** $8·46 + 1·72 = 10·18$ **9.** $5·36 + 3·81 = 9·17$

10. $2·78 + 1·46 = 4·24$ **11.** $3·59 + 1·76 = 5·35$ **12.** $2·83 + 1·97 = 4·80$

Photocopy Masters

Adding decimal numbers

1.
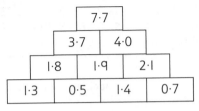

2.
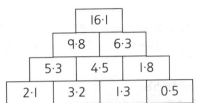

3.
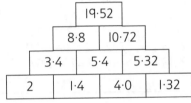

4.
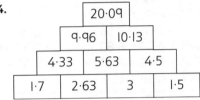

5.
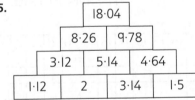

6.
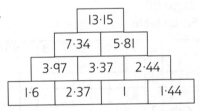

---

page 53

Addition/subtraction N25

Taking away

1. $518 - 373 = 145$
2. $839 - 167 = 672$
3. $625 - 252 = 373$
4. $747 - 583 = 164$
5. $952 - 476 = 476$
6. $711 - 354 = 357$
7. $633 - 297 = 336$
8. $545 - 168 = 377$

---

page 55

Addition/subtraction N25

Ordering subtractions

$4163 - 2827 = 1336$ $3958 - 1746 = 2212$ $9760 - 5409 = 4351$
$5381 - 1256 = 4125$ $6309 - 4582 = 1727$ $4382 - 1751 = 2631$
$7497 - 2862 = 4635$ $8942 - 4089 = 4853$ $6543 - 3906 = 2637$
$6359 - 2856 = 3503$ $7275 - 4493 = 2782$ $8671 - 4725 = 3946$

Photocopy Masters

page 56
Subtracting decimals

1. $4{\cdot}36 - 1{\cdot}49 = 2{\cdot}87$
2. $2{\cdot}54 - 1{\cdot}77 = 0{\cdot}77$
3. $3{\cdot}29 - 2{\cdot}54 = 0{\cdot}75$
4. $1{\cdot}36 - 0{\cdot}48 = 0{\cdot}88$
5. $9{\cdot}27 - 3{\cdot}69 = 5{\cdot}58$
6. $6{\cdot}58 - 5{\cdot}79 = 0{\cdot}79$
7. $5{\cdot}34 - 2{\cdot}88 = 2{\cdot}46$
8. $7{\cdot}05 - 4{\cdot}29 = 2{\cdot}76$

page 58
Subtracting decimals

$3{\cdot}28 - 1{\cdot}47 = 1{\cdot}81$ $4{\cdot}56 - 2{\cdot}68 = 1{\cdot}88$ $2{\cdot}34 - 0{\cdot}77 = 1{\cdot}57$

$9{\cdot}86 - 4{\cdot}95 = 4{\cdot}91$ $7{\cdot}41 - 3{\cdot}59 = 3{\cdot}82$ $8{\cdot}37 - 5{\cdot}43 = 2{\cdot}94$

$5{\cdot}22 - 2{\cdot}66 = 2{\cdot}56$ $6{\cdot}16 - 4{\cdot}75 = 1{\cdot}41$ $3{\cdot}37 - 1{\cdot}82 = 1{\cdot}55$

$4{\cdot}42 - 0{\cdot}59 = 3{\cdot}83$ $9{\cdot}33 - 6{\cdot}75 = 2{\cdot}58$ $7{\cdot}12 - 2{\cdot}53 = 4{\cdot}59$

$8{\cdot}45 - 5{\cdot}78 = 2{\cdot}67$ $6{\cdot}37 - 3{\cdot}98 = 2{\cdot}39$ $2{\cdot}14 - 1{\cdot}47 = 0{\cdot}67$

$5{\cdot}04 - 0{\cdot}36 = 4{\cdot}68$

page 60
Factor table

	1	2	3	4	5	6	7	8	9	10	11	12	13	14	15	16	17	18	19	20	21	22	23	24
1	1																							
2	1	2																						
3	1		3																					
4	1	2		4																				
5	1				5																			
6	1	2	3			6																		
7	1						7																	
8	1	2		4				8																
9	1		3						9															
10	1	2			5					10														
11	1										11													
12	1	2	3	4		6						12												

Properties of number **N27**

	1	2	3	4	5	6	7	8	9	10	11	12	13	14	15	16	17	18	19	20
13	1												13							
14	1	2					7							14						
15	1		3		5										15					
16	1	2		4				8								16				
17	1																17			
18	1	2	3			6			9									18		
19	1																		19	
20	1	2		4	5					10										20

---

page 61
Prime numbers

Properties of number **N28**

1	2	3	4	5	6	7	8	9	10
11	12	13	14	15	16	17	18	19	20
21	22	23	24	25	26	27	28	29	30
31	32	33	34	35	36	37	38	39	40
41	42	43	44	45	46	47	48	49	50
51	52	53	54	55	56	57	58	59	60
61	62	63	64	65	66	67	68	69	70
71	72	73	74	75	76	77	78	79	80
81	82	83	84	85	86	87	88	89	90
91	92	93	94	95	96	97	98	99	100

Unshaded numbers are all prime.

---

page 62
Sets of prime numbers

Properties of number **N28**

Answers will vary.
Possible to use all cards in one set, e.g. 2, 3, 5, 47, 61, 89.

Photocopy Masters

page 63
The 1 to 16 puzzle

	less than 7	between 11 and 17	less than 12	factors of 36
odd numbers	1	15	7 or 11	9
even numbers	2, 4 or 6	14 or 16	8 or 10	4, 6 or 12
multiples of 2	2, 4 or 6	14 or 16	8 or 10	4, 6 or 12
prime numbers	5	13	7 or 11	3

page 64
Positives and negatives

1. 4 and 2   d = 2
2. 5 and 10   d = 5
3. 0 and 7   d = 7
4. −3 and 0   d = 3
5. −5 and −2   d = 3
6. −7 and 1   d = 8
7. 2 and −3   d = 5
8. 3 and 6   d = 3
9. 1 and −9   d = 8
10. −8 and 4   d = 12
11. −10 and 10   d = 20
12. 6 and −1   d = 7
13. −5 and 1   d = 6
14. −3 and −8   d = 5
15. 4 and 7   d = 3
16. −4 and 7   d = 11
17. −7 and 4   d = 11
18. −7 and −4   d = 3

page 65
Difference tables

d	1	3	2	4	5
−2	3	5	4	6	7
−3	4	6	5	7	8
−1	2	4	3	5	6
−5	6	8	7	9	10
−4	5	7	6	8	9

d	1	−3	2	−4	0
3	2	6	1	7	3
−1	2	2	3	3	1
2	1	5	0	6	2
−2	3	1	4	2	2
5	4	8	3	9	5

d	−5	5	−6	7	−8
3	8	2	9	4	11
−4	1	9	2	11	4
2	7	3	8	5	10
−7	2	12	1	14	1
6	11	1	12	1	14

d	−10	0	4	−2	7
−5	5	5	9	3	12
3	13	3	1	5	4
−1	9	1	5	1	8
9	19	9	5	11	2
−3	7	3	7	1	10

Photocopy Masters

Place-value **N30**

Estimating, then multiplying

$29 \times 20 = 580$

$20 \times 61 = 1220$

$49 \times 30 = 1470$

$79 \times 33 = 2607$

$33 \times 30 = 990$

$25 \times 21 = 525$

$22 \times 19 = 418$

$41 \times 20 = 820$

$15 \times 39 = 585$

$51 \times 71 = 3621$

---

page 67
Multiplication/division **N31**

Dice multiplying

All possible solutions are listed.

1. $2 \times 2 \cdot 7 = 5 \cdot 4$
   $5 \times 2 \cdot 7 = 13 \cdot 5$

   $3 \times 2 \cdot 7 = 8 \cdot 1$
   $6 \times 2 \cdot 7 = 16 \cdot 2$

   $4 \times 2 \cdot 7 = 10 \cdot 8$

2. $2 \times 3 \cdot 1 = 6 \cdot 2$
   $5 \times 3 \cdot 1 = 15 \cdot 5$

   $3 \times 3 \cdot 1 = 9 \cdot 3$
   $6 \times 3 \cdot 1 = 18 \cdot 6$

   $4 \times 3 \cdot 1 = 12 \cdot 4$

3. $2 \times 8 \cdot 4 = 16 \cdot 8$
   $5 \times 8 \cdot 4 = 42 \cdot 0$

   $3 \times 8 \cdot 4 = 25 \cdot 2$
   $6 \times 8 \cdot 4 = 50 \cdot 4$

   $4 \times 8 \cdot 4 = 33 \cdot 6$

4. $2 \times 7 \cdot 3 = 14 \cdot 6$
   $5 \times 7 \cdot 3 = 36 \cdot 5$

   $3 \times 7 \cdot 3 = 21 \cdot 9$
   $6 \times 7 \cdot 3 = 43 \cdot 8$

   $4 \times 7 \cdot 3 = 29 \cdot 2$

5. $2 \times 4 \cdot 9 = 9 \cdot 8$
   $5 \times 4 \cdot 9 = 24 \cdot 5$

   $3 \times 4 \cdot 9 = 14 \cdot 7$
   $6 \times 4 \cdot 9 = 29 \cdot 4$

   $4 \times 4 \cdot 9 = 19 \cdot 6$

6. $2 \times 5 \cdot 8 = 11 \cdot 6$
   $5 \times 5 \cdot 8 = 29$

   $3 \times 5 \cdot 8 = 17 \cdot 4$
   $6 \times 5 \cdot 8 = 34 \cdot 8$

   $4 \times 5 \cdot 8 = 23 \cdot 2$

7. $2 \times 9 \cdot 2 = 18 \cdot 4$
   $5 \times 9 \cdot 2 = 46$

   $3 \times 9 \cdot 2 = 27 \cdot 6$
   $6 \times 9 \cdot 2 = 55 \cdot 2$

   $4 \times 9 \cdot 2 = 36 \cdot 8$

8. $2 \times 6 \cdot 6 = 13 \cdot 2$
   $5 \times 6 \cdot 6 = 33 \cdot 0$

   $3 \times 6 \cdot 6 = 19 \cdot 8$
   $6 \times 6 \cdot 6 = 39 \cdot 6$

   $4 \times 6 \cdot 6 = 26 \cdot 4$

9. $2 \times 3 \cdot 7 = 7 \cdot 4$
   $5 \times 3 \cdot 7 = 18 \cdot 5$

   $3 \times 3 \cdot 7 = 11 \cdot 1$
   $6 \times 3 \cdot 7 = 22 \cdot 2$

   $4 \times 3 \cdot 7 = 14 \cdot 8$

10. $2 \times 9 \cdot 9 = 19 \cdot 8$
    $5 \times 9 \cdot 9 = 49 \cdot 5$

    $3 \times 9 \cdot 9 = 29 \cdot 7$
    $6 \times 9 \cdot 9 = 59 \cdot 4$

    $4 \times 9 \cdot 9 = 39 \cdot 6$

---

page 68
Multiplication/division **N31**

Target multiplication

Children's answers will vary.

Best possible answers:

24   $3 \times 7 \cdot 98 = 23 \cdot 94$ difference 0·06

30   $4 \times 7 \cdot 51 = 30 \cdot 04$ difference 0·04

18   $5 \times 3 \cdot 61 = 18 \cdot 05$ difference 0·05

Photocopy Masters

page 68 cont ...

38	$8 \times 4.75 = 38$	difference 0
9.5	$2 \times 4.75 = 9.5$	difference 0
12	$2 \times 5.98 = 11.96$	difference 0.04
51	$9 \times 5.67 = 51.03$	difference 0.03
29	$4 \times 7.25 = 29$	difference 0

---

page 69
Multiplying decimals

1. $4 \times 1.7 = 6.8$
2. $5 \times 2.8 = 14$
3. $6 \times 3.9 = 23.4$
4. $3 \times 4.53 = 13.59$
5. $7 \times 1.62 = 11.34$
6. $5 \times 2.84 = 14.2$
7. $4 \times 7.36 = 29.44$
8. $6 \times 2.81 = 16.86$
9. $8 \times 5.74 = 45.92$

---

page 70
Dividing

1. $425 \div 17 = 25$
2. $234 \div 13 = 18$
3. $608 \div 19 = 32$
4. $688 \div 16 = 43$
5. $672 \div 24 = 28$
6. $432 \div 27 = 16$
7. $696 \div 29 = 24$
8. $612 \div 36 = 17$
9. $624 \div 48 = 13$

---

page 71
Football attendances

Premier league	$202\,000 \div 7 = 28\,857$	(To the nearest whole number)
Division 1	$104\,000 \div 7 = 14\,857$	(To the nearest whole number)
Division 2	$57\,000 \div 9 = 6333$	(To the nearest whole number)
Division 3	$39\,800 \div 10 = 3980$	

---

page 73
Dividing decimals

1. $8.4 \div 2 = 4.2$
2. $9.6 \div 3 = 3.2$
3. $8.8 \div 4 = 2.2$
4. $5.6 \div 2 = 2.8$
5. $9.5 \div 5 = 1.9$
6. $12.6 \div 6 = 2.1$
7. $14.4 \div 4 = 3.6$
8. $16.5 \div 5 = 3.3$
9. $23.8 \div 7 = 3.4$
10. $18.9 \div 3 = 6.3$
11. $27.4 \div 2 = 13.7$
12. $51.2 \div 8 = 6.4$
13. $55.8 \div 6 = 9.3$
14. $43.4 \div 7 = 6.2$
15. $87.3 \div 9 = 9.7$

Photocopy Masters

page 74

Dividing decimals

1. $4·8 ÷ 2 = 2·4$
2. $5·6 ÷ 4 = 1·4$
3. $7·6 ÷ 2 = 3·8$
4. $9·5 ÷ 5 = 1·9$
5. $8·4 ÷ 6 = 1·4$
6. $3·5 ÷ 7 = 0·5$
7. $7·0 ÷ 10 = 0·7$
8. $6·4 ÷ 8 = 0·8$
9. $9·9 ÷ 9 = 1·1$
10. $8·4 ÷ 7 = 1·2$
11. $8·5 ÷ 5 = 1·7$
12. $7·6 ÷ 4 = 1·9$
13. $8·4 ÷ 6 = 1·4$
14. $6·9 ÷ 3 = 2·3$
15. $9·6 ÷ 8 = 1·2$

page 75

Percentages

1. 25%   2. 62%   3. 19%   4. 37%   5. 76%   6. 91%

7. 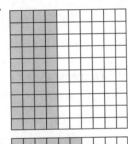   8. 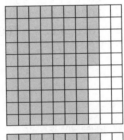   9.

10. 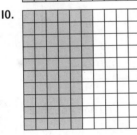   11. 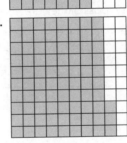   12.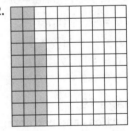

page 76

Percentages

1. teams scoring 0 goals — 10% (5 in 50 teams)
2. teams scoring 1 goal — 28%
3. teams scoring 2 goals — 24%
4. teams scoring 3 goals — 20%
5. teams scoring 4 goals — 14%
6. teams scoring 5 goals — 4%
7. teams scoring more than 2 goals — 38%
8. teams scoring fewer than 2 goals — 38%

Photocopy Masters

page 76 cont ...

Percentages **N35**

9. drawn matches — 24% (6 in 25 matches)
10. matches with fewer than 4 goals — 32% (8 in 25 matches)
11. matches with more than 5 goals — 32%

---

page 77
Percentages

Percentages **N35**

1. 10% of £20 = £2
2. 20% of £50 = £10
3. 50% of £40 = £20
4. 100% of £60 = £60
5. 30% of £30 = £9
6. 40% of £100 = £40
7. 25% of £80 = £20
8. 75% of £4 = £3
9. 80% of £50 = £40
10. 10% of £25 = £2.50
11. 30% of £100 = £30
12. 60% of £10 = £6
13. 50% of £20 = £10
14. 20% of £20 = £4
15. 90% of £10 = £9
16. 60% of £5 = £3
17. 30% of £40 = £12
18. 5% of £20 = £1
19. 50% of £120 = £60
20. 75% of £80 = £60

---

page 78
Fractions and decimals

Fractions/decimals **N36**

Children's answers will vary.
Using each number once only, possibilities are:

$0 \cdot 2 = \frac{1}{5}$ $0 \cdot 4 = \frac{2}{5}$ $0 \cdot 5 = \frac{1}{2}$ $0 \cdot 5 = \frac{2}{4}$ $0 \cdot 5 = \frac{3}{6}$ $0 \cdot 6 = \frac{3}{5}$ $0 \cdot 8 = \frac{4}{5}$

$1 \cdot 2 = \frac{6}{5}$ $1 \cdot 4 = \frac{7}{5}$ $1 \cdot 5 = \frac{3}{2}$ $1 \cdot 5 = \frac{6}{4}$ $1 \cdot 6 = \frac{8}{5}$ $1 \cdot 8 = \frac{9}{5}$

$2 \cdot 0 = \frac{6}{3}$ $2 \cdot 0 = \frac{8}{4}$ $3 \cdot 0 = \frac{6}{2}$ $4 \cdot 0 = \frac{8}{2}$ $3 \cdot 5 = \frac{7}{2}$ $4 \cdot 5 = \frac{9}{2}$

---

page 79
Fractions and percentages

Fractions/decimals **N36**

1. $\frac{1}{10}$ = 10%
2. $\frac{1}{100}$ = 1%
3. $\frac{1}{20}$ = 5%
4. $\frac{1}{2}$ = 50%
5. $\frac{1}{4}$ = 25%
6. $\frac{1}{5}$ = 20%
7. $\frac{3}{10}$ = 30%
8. $\frac{3}{4}$ = 75%
9. $\frac{2}{5}$ = 40%
10. $\frac{1}{50}$ = 2%
11. $\frac{11}{20}$ = 55%
12. $\frac{1}{25}$ = 4%
13. $\frac{9}{10}$ = 90%
14. $\frac{4}{5}$ = 80%
15. $\frac{17}{50}$ = 34%
16. $\frac{7}{10}$ = 70%
17. $\frac{6}{10}$ = 60%
18. $\frac{2}{50}$ = 4%
19. $\frac{6}{25}$ = 24%
20. $\frac{3}{5}$ = 60%

---

page 80
Fractions, percentages and decimals

Fractions/decimals **N36**

1. $\frac{16}{100}$ < 60%
2. 30% = 0·3
3. 0·4 > $\frac{4}{100}$
4. $\frac{1}{4}$ < 40%

Photocopy Masters

page 80 cont ...

Fractions/decimals **N36**

5. $50\% = \frac{5}{10}$ **6.** $\frac{7}{10} < 0.72$ **7.** $0.55 > \frac{1}{2}$ **8.** $60\% = \frac{6}{10}$

9. $\frac{5}{10} > 25\%$ **10.** $\frac{4}{5} = 0.8$ **11.** $40\% < \frac{4}{5}$ **12.** $\frac{18}{100} < 80\%$

13. $\frac{9}{10} < 0.91$ **14.** $70\% = \frac{70}{100}$ **15.** $0.64 < 65\%$ **16.** $\frac{8}{10} > 75\%$

17. $\frac{1}{10} = 0.1$ **18.** $1.2 > \frac{5}{10}$ **19.** $80\% > \frac{8}{100}$ **20.** $1.0 = 100\%$

---

page 81

Ratio/proportion **N37**

Proportion

1. $\frac{8}{24} = \frac{1}{3}$ **2.** $\frac{6}{12} = \frac{1}{2}$ **3.** $\frac{4}{6} = \frac{2}{3}$ **4.** $\frac{12}{20} = \frac{3}{5}$ **5.** $\frac{3}{9} = \frac{1}{3}$

6. $\frac{6}{16} = \frac{3}{8}$ **7.** $\frac{3}{10}$ **8.** $\frac{6}{15} = \frac{2}{5}$ **9.** $\frac{4}{12} = \frac{1}{3}$ **10.** $\frac{8}{12} = \frac{2}{3}$

11. $\frac{12}{16} = \frac{3}{4}$ **12.** $\frac{10}{25} = \frac{2}{5}$

---

page 82

Ratio/proportion **N37**

Proportion

1. $\frac{6}{12} = \frac{1}{2}$ **2.** $\frac{1}{10}$ **3.** $\frac{3}{9} = \frac{1}{3}$ **4.** $\frac{4}{12} = \frac{1}{3}$ **5.** $\frac{5}{10} = \frac{1}{2}$

6. $\frac{4}{8} = \frac{1}{2}$ **7.** $\frac{3}{12} = \frac{1}{4}$ **8.** $\frac{2}{10} = \frac{1}{5}$ **9.** $\frac{8}{10} = \frac{4}{5}$ **10.** $\frac{2}{12} = \frac{1}{6}$

11. $\frac{0}{9} = 0$ **12.** $\frac{2}{8} = \frac{1}{4}$ **13.** $\frac{6}{12} = \frac{1}{2}$ **14.** $\frac{1}{10}$ **15.** $\frac{2}{8} = \frac{1}{4}$

16. $\frac{6}{9} = \frac{2}{3}$ **17.** $\frac{3}{10}$ **18.** $\frac{3}{12} = \frac{1}{4}$

---

page 83

Ratio/proportion **N38**

Ratio

1. 4:1 **2.** 4:3 **3.** 1:3 **4.** 5:1 **5.** 2:3

6. 3:2 **7.** 4:3 **8.** 30:7

---

page 84

Ratio/proportion **N38**

Ratio

1. 6 squares shaded **2.** 4 squares shaded **3.** 2 squares shaded

4. 8 squares shaded **5.** 5 squares shaded **6.** 3 squares shaded

7. 6 squares shaded **8.** 10 squares shaded **9.** 15 squares shaded

10. 6 squares shaded **11.** 10 squares shaded

Photocopy Masters

page 85
Checking calculations

1. $38 + 76 = 114$ correct

2. $143 + 59 = 202$ correct

3. $16 + 7·9 = 23·9$ correct

4. $42·2 - 19 = 23·2$ $25·2 + 19 = 42·2$

5. $5·8 + 7·7 = 13·5$ correct

6. $2·8 + 3·65 = 6·45$ correct

7. $5·45 + 13·9 = 19·35$ $19·15 - 13·9 = 5·25$

8. $4·28 + 7·63 = 11·91$ correct

9. $2·08 + 4·96 = 7·04$ correct

10. $9·67 + 7·7 = 17·37$ correct

page 86
Using arithmetical facts

1. $2·4 + 7·6 = 10·0$

2. $5·8 + 3·72 = 9·52$

3. $6·43 + 5·78 = 12·21$

4. $5·34 + 6·09 = 11·43$

5. $8·63 - 2·71 = 5·92$

6. $9·6 - 3·7 = 5·9$

7. $12·3 - 4·16 = 8·14$

8. $7·52 - 1·9 = 5·62$

9. $8·31 - 0·78 = 7·53$

10. $9 - 4·38 = 4·62$

page 87
Squares and square roots

1. $1 \times 1 = 1$ $\sqrt{1} = 1$

2. $2 \times 2 = 4$ $\sqrt{4} = 2$

3. $3 \times 3 = 9$ $\sqrt{9} = 3$

4. $4 \times 4 = 16$ $\sqrt{16} = 4$

5. $5 \times 5 = 25$ $\sqrt{25} = 5$

6. $6 \times 6 = 36$ $\sqrt{36} = 6$

7. $7 \times 7 = 49$ $\sqrt{49} = 7$

8. $8 \times 8 = 64$ $\sqrt{64} = 8$

9. $9 \times 9 = 81$ $\sqrt{81} = 9$

10. $10 \times 10 = 100$ $\sqrt{100} = 10$

11. $11 \times 11 = 121$ $\sqrt{121} = 11$

12. $12 \times 12 = 144$ $\sqrt{144} = 12$

13. $20 \times 20 = 400$ $\sqrt{400} = 20$

14. $30 \times 30 = 900$ $\sqrt{900} = 30$

15. $40 \times 40 = 1600$ $\sqrt{1600} = 40$

page 88
Squares

$15^2 = 225$ $25^2 = 625$ $35^2 = 1225$ $45^2 = 2025$ $55^2 = 3025$

$65^2 = 4225$ $75^2 = 5625$ $85^2 = 7225$ $95^2 = 9025$

To square a 2-digit number with a units digit of 5, multiply the first digit by the next consecutive number to find the first one or two digits of the answer. The last two digits are always 25.

Photocopy Masters

page 89

Square root estimating

$\sqrt{64} = 8$ $\sqrt{121} = 11$ $\sqrt{400} = 20$ $\sqrt{900} = 30$ $\sqrt{1225} = 35$

$\sqrt{2916} = 54$ $\sqrt{3249} = 57$ $\sqrt{5329} = 73$ $\sqrt{729} = 27$ $\sqrt{3136} = 56$

page 90

Pascal's triangle

Next three lines:

```
        1    5    10   10    5    1
      1    6    15   20   15    6    1
    1    7    21   35   35   21    7    1
```

Each number is the sum of the two above it.

page 91

Digit patterns

2-digit numbers – answer is always 22
3-digit numbers – answer is always 222

page 92

Odds and evens

1. $O + E = O$
2. $E - O = O$
3. $O \times O = O$
4. $E \times E = E$
5. $O \times E = E$
6. $O \times E \times O = E$
7. $E \times E \times O = E$
8. $O \times (E + O) = O$
9. $E \times (O + O) = E$
10. $(O - E) \times O = O$
11. $(O - O) \times E = E$
12. $(O + E) \times (E - O) = O$
13. $(E - E) \times (O - O) = E$
14. $(E + O) \times (E - O) = O$
15. $(O - E) \times (E - O) = O$
16. $(O \times E) + (E \times E) = E$

page 94

Yards, feet, inches, metres, centimetres

1. 3 feet = 1 yard
2. 10 inches $> \frac{1}{2}$ foot
3. 8 feet < 3 yards
4. $1\frac{1}{2}$ yards > 4 feet
5. 40 inches $< 1\frac{1}{2}$ yards
6. $2\frac{1}{2}$ feet < 32 inches
7. $\frac{1}{2}$ yard < 20 inches
8. $5\frac{1}{2}$ feet < 2 yards
9. 120 inches > 3 yards
10. 4 feet < 50 inches
11. 12 inches = 1 foot
12. 30 inches $= 2\frac{1}{2}$ feet
13. 4 metres > 12 feet
14. 6 inches < 18 cm
15. 50 cm < 2 feet
16. $1\frac{1}{2}$ yards > 110 cm

Photocopy Masters

page 95
Pounds, ounces, grams, kilograms

1. 2 lb < 1 kg
2. 400 g < 1 lb
3. 30 oz < 1 kg
4. 2 lb > 30 oz
5. 1000 g = 1 kg
6. $\frac{1}{4}$ lb < 6 oz
7. $\frac{1}{2}$ kg > 1 lb
8. 9 oz > $\frac{1}{2}$ lb
9. 200 g < 10 oz
10. 750 g > $1\frac{1}{2}$ lb
11. $\frac{1}{4}$ kg < 10 oz
12. $\frac{1}{2}$ lb < 300 g
13. 45 oz < 3 lb 2 oz
14. 600 g < 1 lb 8 oz
15. 4 kg < 10 lb
16. $2\frac{1}{2}$ kg > 72 oz

page 96
Pints, gallons, litres, centilitres, millilitres

1. 1 gallon = 8 pints
2. 12 pints = $1\frac{1}{2}$ gallons
3. 1 litre = 1000 ml
4. 1 litre = 100 cl
5. 1 cl = 10 ml
6. 500 ml = $\frac{1}{2}$ litre
7. 300 ml = 30 cl
8. $\frac{1}{2}$ litre = 50 cl
9. $2\frac{1}{2}$ gallons = 20 pints
10. 1 litre ≈ $1\frac{3}{4}$ pints
11. 1 gallon ≈ 4·5 litres
12. 45 cl = 450 ml
13. 4 litres ≈ 7 pints
14. 9 litres ≈ 2 gallons
15. 1·3 litres = 130 cl
16. 4·5 cl = 45 ml
17. 5·3 litres = 5300 ml
18. 150 ml = 0·150 litres

page 97
Area of a rectangle

1	2	3	4	5	6	7	8	9	10
2	4	6	8	10	12	14	16	18	20
3	6	9	12	15	18	21	24	27	30
4	8	12	16	20	24	28	32	36	40
5	10	15	20	25	30	35	40	45	50
6	12	18	24	30	36	42	48	54	60
7	14	21	28	35	42	49	56	63	70
8	16	24	32	40	48	56	64	72	80
9	18	27	36	45	54	63	72	91	90
10	20	30	40	50	60	70	80	90	100

The grid is a multiplication square.

Photocopy Masters

page 98
Surface area

Cuboid	Area of top (cm²)	Area of side (cm²)	Area of front (cm²)	Total surface area (cm²)
A	6	3	2	22
B	10	10	4	48
C	9	9	9	54
D	32	40	20	184
E	30	18	15	126
F	12	8	6	52

page 99
Area of a right-angled triangle

1. 10 cm²   **2.** 14 cm²   **3.** 15 cm²   **4.** 36 cm²
5. 9 cm²   **6.** 18 cm²   **7.** 12 cm²   **8.** 25 cm²

page 100
Area

A   13·5 cm²   B   20 cm²   C   12 cm²   D   13·5 cm²
E   18 cm²
F   18 cm²   G   12 cm²   H   16 cm²
C and G, A and D, H, E and F, B

page 101
Perimeter

6·7 cm + 8·8 cm + 7·1 cm + 15 cm = 37·6 cm
6·1 cm + 4·9 cm + 5·5 cm + 6·4 cm + 5·2 cm = 28·1 cm
17·8 cm + 7·6 cm + 16·1 cm = 41·5 cm

page 102
Angles at a point

1. 47°, 133°, 47°, 133°   **2.** 146°, 34°, 146°, 34°   **3.** 87°, 93°, 87°, 93°
4. 16°, 164°, 16°, 164°   **5.** 139°, 41°, 139°, 41°

Photocopy Masters

page 103
Angles of a triangle

I. 50°, 90° 2. 25°, 90° 3. 18°, 90° 4. 58° 5. 38°
6. 37° 7. 67° 8. 11° 9. 53°, 90° 10. 91°

page 104
Angles in polygons

number of sides/name	number of right angles	degrees
3, triangle	2	180
4, quadrilateral	4	360
5, pentagon	6	540
6, hexagon	8	720

page 106
Road signs

The following have line symmetry:
2, 5, 8, 11, 12

page 107
Reflections

I. x-axis 2. y-axis 3. y-axis 4. x-axis 5. y-axis
6. x- and y-axis 7. y-axis 8. x-axis 9. y-axis 10. x- and y-axis

page 108
Translations

I. (0,3) 2. (2,$^-$3) 3. (4,$^-$4) 4. (5,7)
5. (0,5) 6. ($^-$5,$^-$6) 7. ($^-$3,$^-$3) 8. (5,2)

9. left 5, down 1 10. right 2, up 7 11. left 6, up 4
12. right 1, down 3 13. left 4, down 4 14. left 4, up 3

page 109
Open cubes

Nets for open cubes are: A, B, D, E, G, I, K, L

Photocopy Masters

page 112
2-d shape **S8**

Shading shapes

Answers will vary.

---

page 113
2-d shape **S8**

Naming shapes

1. rectangle	2. rectangle	3. triangle	4. rhombus
5. pentagon	6. pentagon	7. pentagon	8. triangle
9. hexagon	10. hexagon		

---

page 115
Grouped data **D1**

Grouped frequencies

| 1. 16 | 2. 6 | 3. 4 | 4. 14 | 5. 9 | 6. 13 |
| 7. 20 | 8. 29 | 9. 36 | 10. 30 | 11. 29 | |

12. 11–20   13. 31–40   14. 41–50   15. 1–10   16. 21–30

17. 49

---

page 118
Pie charts **D2**

Favourite pets

dog 150°
cat 105°
rabbit 75°
bird 30°

---

page 119
Conversion graphs **D3**

Inches and centimetres

Answers will vary.

---

page 120
Averages **D4**

Averages

		mean
8	10	9
4	6	5

		mean
3	5	4
2	8	5

			mean
3	4	5	4
2	6	1	3
1	3	2	2

			mean
5	4	9	6
3	6	9	6
5	4	6	5

				mean
3	2	4	7	4
2	3	2	5	3
4	5	6	5	5
1	0	3	4	2

				mean
3	7	6	8	6
5	8	9	10	8
10	5	15	10	10
4	6	8	10	7

page 121
Card averages

Using two cards:

mean 2	2, 2		
mean 3	2, 4		
mean 4	2, 6	4, 4	
mean 5	2, 8	4, 6	
mean 6	2, 10	4, 8	6, 6
mean 7	4, 10	6, 8	
mean 8	6, 10	8, 8	
mean 9	8, 10		
mean 10	10, 10		

Using three cards:

mean 2	2, 2, 2			
mean 3	not possible			
mean 4	2, 2, 8	2, 4, 6	4, 4, 4	
mean 5	not possible			
mean 6	2, 6, 10	2, 8, 8,	4, 6, 8	6, 6, 6
mean 7	not possible			
mean 8	4, 10, 10	6, 8, 10	8, 8, 8	
mean 9	not possible			
mean 10	10, 10, 10			

Photocopy Masters

page 122
Probability

1. $\frac{2}{6} = \frac{1}{3}$ 2. $\frac{4}{6} = \frac{2}{3}$ 3. $\frac{2}{6} = \frac{1}{3}$ 4. $\frac{4}{6} = \frac{2}{3}$ 5. $\frac{2}{6} = \frac{1}{3}$

6. $\frac{2}{6} = \frac{1}{3}$ 7. $\frac{1}{6}$ 8. $\frac{2}{6} = \frac{1}{3}$ 9. $\frac{3}{6} = \frac{1}{2}$ 10. $\frac{3}{6} = \frac{1}{2}$

11. $\frac{3}{6} = \frac{1}{2}$ 12. $\frac{5}{6}$ 13. $\frac{2}{6} = \frac{1}{3}$ 14. $\frac{1}{6}$ 15. $\frac{2}{6} = \frac{1}{3}$

16. $\frac{5}{6}$ 17. $\frac{3}{6} = \frac{1}{2}$ 18. $\frac{4}{6} = \frac{2}{3}$

---

page 124
Solving problems (1)

Mixed problems

1. 4 passengers $\times$ 3 = 12 passengers
2. £5·50 $\times$ 2 = £11·00
3. 3 tickets $\times$ 4 = 12 tickets   12 + 1 = 13 tickets
4. David 1·36 m – 1·26 m = 0·10 m   John 1·27 m – 1·19 m = 0·08 m
   David has grown more.
5. 10:00 – 6:45 = 3hr 15 min   110 min + 90 min = 200 min = 3 hr 20 min
   She cannot watch them both.
6. 450 ml $\div$ 5 = 90 ml
7. (£10 $\times$ 2) + £7·50 = £27·50   £27·50 – £15·98 = £11·52   £11·52 $\div$ 2 = £5·76
   They each have £5·76.
8.–9. Answers will vary.

---

page 125
Solving problems (2)

Mixed problems

1. £2·50 $\times$ 5 = £12·50   £12·50 – (£1·25 + £0·65) = £10·60 left at the end of
   the day.
2. Benji 42 min; Sarah 57 min; Mariah 49 min; Zach 43 min
   Race order: Benji; Zach (1 min behind winner), Mariah (7 min behind
   winner), Sarah (15 min behind winner)
3. £10 – (£3 $\div$ 2) – (£2 $\times$ 2) – £0·50 = £10 – £1·50 – £4 – £0·50 = £4 left each
   £4 – £2·50 = £1·50 They can have 1 turn each on the Water Chute.
4. 21 accepted + 16 extra friends = 37 planned   37 – 8 = 29
   29 people are actually at the party.

---

page 126
Solving problems (3)

Mixed problems

1. (2 + 8) $\times$ 10 = 100 2. (5 + 7) $\times$ 3 = 36 3. (12 – 3) $\div$ 3 = 3
4. (4 $\times$ 2) + 26 = 34 5. (8 + 2) $\times$ 22 = 220 6. (34 – 8) $\times$ 5 = 130

Photocopy Masters

page 126 cont ...

7. $10 \times (16 + 4) = 200$ **8.** $(2 \times 3) + 24 = 30$ **9.** $(32 - 16) \times 2 = 32$
10. $(4 + 4) \times 4 = 32$ **11.** $(12 + 8) \times 4 = 80$ **12.** $17 - (2 \times 8) = 1$
13. $29 + (3 \times 8) = 53$ **14.** $(16 \div 8) \times 44 = 88$ **15.** $(32 \div 4) - 4 = 4$
16. $(10 \times 9) - 9 = 81$ **17.** $(2 + 6) \times (3 + 2) = 40$

18. $14 + 6 = 20$ sweets $20 \div 4 = 5$ 5 sweets per box
19. $32 + 8 = 40$ $40 \div 10 = 4$ 4 balls per tube
20. £20 − (£2 + £7) = £11 £11 ÷ 2 = £5·50 Each light costs £2·50.
21. 3 stickers × 8 = 24 stickers He had $24 + 6 = 30$ stickers to start with.
  $30 \div 5 = 6$ He bought 6 packets.
22. 15 miles − (4 miles × 2) = 7 miles 7 miles ÷ 2 = 3·5 miles

---

page 127

Solving problems (4)

1. multiple of 11 and 6 therefore multiple of 66 $66 \times 3 = 198$ (divisible by 9)
2. $106 - (47 + 29 + 13) = 17$ 17 pictures are of other pets.
3. Kelly has $\frac{2}{3}$ of 24 sweets = 16 sweets

  Jamie has $\frac{1}{3}$ of 24 sweets = 8 sweets
4. 120
5. 10% of 50 = 5 $35 - 5 = 30$ $30 = \frac{2}{3}$ of 45 Mystery number = 45
6. $16 - 25 + 19 = 10$ ($16 = 4^2$, ⁻25 factor of 5, 19 prime)
7. $\frac{5}{7}$ of album is colour, $\frac{5}{7}$ of 56 = 40 There are 40 colour pictures.
8. $27·5 \div 5 = 5·5$ $5·5 - 4·6 = 0·9$ mystery number = 0·9